EARLY EXPERIENCE AND THE ORGANIZATION OF BEHAVIOR

DEVELOPMENTAL PROCESSES
AND BEHAVIOR SERIES

edited by

SHELDON H. WHITE
BARBARA NOTKIN WHITE

EARLY EXPERIENCE AND THE ORGANIZATION OF BEHAVIOR

JOHN PAUL SCOTT

Bowling Green State University

Brooks/Cole Publishing Company

A Division of Wadsworth Publishing Company, Inc.

Acknowledgments

The following materials in this book are repro-
duced by permission of the authors and
publishers:

Table 2.1 and Figure 1.1 from Scott (1963)
by permission of the Society for Research
in Child Development.

Figure 2.1 by permission of Daniel G. Freedman.

Part of Figure 1.3 (cover picture of *Science*,
Vol. 138, Nov. 30, 1962) and Figure
4.1 from Scott (1962), by permission
of the American Association for the
Advancement of Science.

Figure 5.2, from Kunst (1948), by permission
of author and the American Psychological
Association.

L.C. Cat. Card No.: 68-12721

Printed in the United States of America

PREFACE

The importance of early experience in determining later behavior has long been an axiom of both folklore and science. We have
a host of proverbs to this effect, ranging from the botanical "As the
twig is bent, so is the tree inclined" to the metaphorical "The child
is father to the man." However, it was not until Freud presented his
theories of emotional development that early experience became a
subject of serious scientific investigation. As a field of human research,
the area immediately presented difficulties. The potential effects of
early experience on human infants are so grave and far-reaching that
most experiments must be ruled out, and the student of human behavior is left to study either the results of unplanned accidents or the
relatively trivial variations in human baby care which are socially
permissible.

For these reasons experimenters began to study animal infancy.
Many of the first experiments by J. McV. Hunt and others were
attempts to test psychoanalytic theories on animals such as rats, but
animal investigation soon uncovered a number of hitherto unsuspected
phenomena which could be pursued in their own right. Among these
were primary socialization, or imprinting, whose general significance
was first appreciated by Konrad Lorenz, and early stimulation, which
has profound effects on the development of the adrenal system. As
data accumulates, we are beginning to organize a science of behavioral
development which extends not only back into prenatal life—where
new data indicates that the emotional state of the mother affects her
offspring—but even further back into the egg, and ultimately to the
genes themselves.

The general scheme of this book is to examine systematically
the various factors in each period of development which immediately

or eventually modify behavior. From this we derive the almost self-evident conclusion that development is best analyzed in terms of processes rather than in terms of static and anatomical concepts. This in turn leads to several general principles concerning the relationship between developmental processes and behavioral organization.

Since so much of the experimental work on early experience has been done with infra-human animals and since the significance of these results can only be appreciated against a background of information regarding the biological nature and development of each species, I have given a brief description of the behavioral development of some of the most commonly used experimental animals. Because it would be impossible to describe all of these animals in detail—and indeed many of them are not known in detail—I have where appropriate used examples from the dog. Thanks to the work done by my former colleagues at the Jackson Laboratory over a period of twenty years, the development of behavior in the dog has been more thoroughly studied than in any other species except man. Furthermore, the early behavior of these two species has much in common, particularly with respect to the development of social relations. It is to be hoped that similarly detailed studies of development will eventually emerge from the current field and laboratory studies of primates, but this will be a long process because of the rarity, difficulty of breeding, and long generation span of these animals.

Space has not permitted the detailed description of every important experiment, or indeed the mention of much important work. I have therefore included a list of references which should be a guide to this information and the growing body of scientific literature on the subject of early experience.

Finally, I wish to thank my wife for helping in the preparation of this manuscript. To her I give credit for any readability it may possess. I also wish to thank Sheldon H. White, Theodore Schaefer, and Bettye M. Caldwell for critical reading of the manuscript.

John Paul Scott

CONTENTS

EARLY EXPERIENCE AND THE ORGANIZATION OF BEHAVIOR

1 ANIMAL INFANCY AND THE EVOLUTION OF BEHAVIORAL DEVELOPMENT

Young animals are always fascinating, partly because such creatures as downy chicks and new-born lambs are physically attractive objects to touch and cuddle, and partly because they behave so differently from their parents. To many people hand-rearing a helpless young animal is a self rewarding occupation, and the custom of picking up young animals as pets is found in any culture, whether civilized or primitive. Hand reared animals often turn out to be very different from their wild relatives and, as a result, hand-rearing is now not

1

only a pleasant pastime but a major scientific technique for exploring the effects of early experience.

The general theory of causation assumes that where two events always follow in sequence, the first may be the cause of the second. The fact that early development precedes later behavior therefore suggests that the study of early experience may provide a key for explaining the adult behavior of any individual. Many scientists have looked to animal species for an explanation of human development, but this is not a simple matter of tracing man's beginnings. When we begin to gather the needed facts we find that the developmental history of different species cannot be arranged in stairstep fashion, beginning with the simplest sort of behavorial development and grandly culminating in that of man, but rather that the development of behavior in other species has evolved in many different directions related to different sorts of social organizations and environmental adaptation. Instead of a history of the evolution of human behavior, the material gives us a picture of human development in perspective with that of other animal species.

Early experience can be studied both descriptively and experimentally. In the great majority of cases, experimental studies have been done on animals other than man because the potentially serious consequences of such experiments cannot be risked with human beings. Most of the work with human infants has therefore been descriptive. On the other hand, descriptive techniques have been seldom employed on other animals until quite recently. The resulting combination of experimental and descriptive techniques has been highly productive. Descriptive studies of infrahuman animals have provided guide lines for human research, and experimental studies have provided new hypotheses and tested old ones. However, the information derived from other species can be safely applied to human beings only if we have a thorough knowledge of both. One of the first things that is apparent from comparisons between species is that the same experience will produce different results in different animals, depending upon the kind of development peculiar to each.

BASIC METHODS OF STUDY

The measurement of age. In the study of development, the primary dimension of behavior is time, and particularly time since the beginning of development. Ideally, development should be measured from the moment when the sperm first enters the egg, but this instant is often difficult to determine, and most measurements of developmental data are based on the time from birth in mammals or from hatching in birds. However, since there is no exact relationship between the moment of conception and the moment of birth, infants are born in a greater or lesser state of maturity.

This leads to considerable inaccuracy in what we call the age of the individual, which, in turn, contributes to variation in degree of development between individuals who are ostensibly the same age. How much individuals vary partly depends upon the length of the normal gestation period. Relatively little variation can occur in mammals like mice, whose young are born in twenty-one days, and a great deal in man, for whom the gestation period is approximately nine months.

Because age as ordinarily measured is inaccurate, it becomes necessary to obtain information on a large number of individuals in order to get a reasonably accurate picture of developmental timing. In a large population we can assume that errors of timing and length of gestation are distributed in the form of normal curves. However, variation in the speed of development itself should not fall into a symmetrical normal curve, because one end of the curve is limited and the other is not. The maximum speed of development has an upper limit, but the minimum speed can be infinitely slow. For example, there is considerable variation in the time at which children begin to walk. Variation is limited on the lower end of the scale, as no child can walk before birth, but is virtually unlimited on the upper end, as a congenitally crippled child may never walk at all.

Therefore, if we wish to express a "usual" age of development for a particular behavior, it is best to compute the median age at which an observed sample shows the behavior rather than to calculate the mean or average age. The median, unlike the mean, does not give exaggerated weight to scores from individuals who develop the behavior very late or not at all. The median score is, of course, identical with the 50th percentile score. A good estimate of range of developmental age is similarly given by the semi-interquartile range, the range of scores between the 25th and 75th percentiles.

Figure 1.1 shows the relationship between an ideal normal curve and the percentile curve. This transformation produces an S-shaped curve with the interesting feature that the portion between

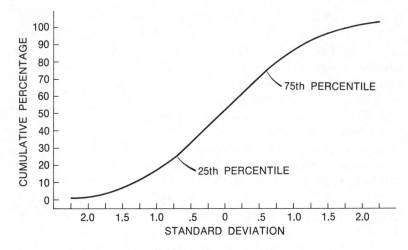

FIGURE 1.1 The normal curve expressed in terms of cumulative percentages. Note that the result is an "S" curve, with the portion between the 25th and 75th percentiles forming very nearly a straight line. Consequently, one of the most useful ways of comparing the development of an individual with a population is in reference to percentiles within this range.

20 and 80 percent is very nearly a straight line. Within these limits the percentile measurement therefore gives an accurate picture of the relative development of an individual in terms of age, as the percentile figure is directly proportional to age. For example, according to the figures now available for the onset of walking, a difference in 10 percentile points below the median means that a child is approximately three weeks ahead of the average child in the population, and a difference of 30 percentile points (the point below which the age relationship does not hold) would mean that he was advanced by nine weeks. Of course, such estimates are meaningful only when they are based on a large and representative sample of the whole population. One of the deficiencies of our present information on human development is that most of it is based on small samples of children belonging to families with middle-class incomes.

We especially need more accurate measurements of the time of appearance of the four groups of basic capacities on which the development of behavior depends.

Sensory capacities. Before behavioral responses can be made, sense organs must be developed to the point where stimuli can be received. The fact than an animal has sense organs does not mean that these are functional, and the only way to be sure is to make various tests. One of the simplest kinds of tests makes use of primary reflexes. For example, when a puppy's eyes have become completely open at approximately thirteen days of age, one can shine a bright light in them and look for the pupillary contraction. A pupillary response gives evidence that light does affect the retina and that the eye is functioning at least in a general way. Similarly, a loud noise will produce a startle response; but this response does not appear until the puppy is about eighteen or nineteen days of age, indicating that auditory capacities appear later than visual ones. In general, reflexes appear first in weak and variable form and after a few days become strong and stable. The onset of a reflex is therefore so gradual that it usually does not give a precisely timed index of development.

The presence of a reflex does not indicate that a sense organ is completely functional. More complex tests must be used in order to show that a young animal has fully developed sensory functions. One of the most interesting devices of this sort is the "visual cliff," which tests whether the developing individual can perceive depth (Walk, 1965). This ingenious device is based on the observation that even young animals are afraid to approach the edge of any steeply descending surface and consequently will not fall over it. The apparatus consists of a deep box covered with a large sheet of plate glass. A patterned surface (such as a sheet of oilcloth with a checkerboard pattern) is visible under the glass. Over one half of the box this sheet is placed directly under the glass. On the other half, it drops sharply down several feet and continues across the bottom half of the box. The animal or baby placed on the center of this apparatus thus gets the impression that he is standing or crawling on the edge of a small cliff, although in fact the glass provides a firm support over everything.

The apparatus can be used on any animal that can see and gives dramatic results with the young of many different species. From the very first day, young sheep and goats will refuse to cross the "deep" side of the apparatus, and if one is placed directly on the glass over the deep area, it will immediately stiffen up in apparent terror and refuse to move.

Obviously, at least two sensory capacities are involved in this behavior. One is the development of the visual sensory capacity for depth perception, and the other is the development of a fear of falling, or perhaps more properly, a fear of depths. Assuming that

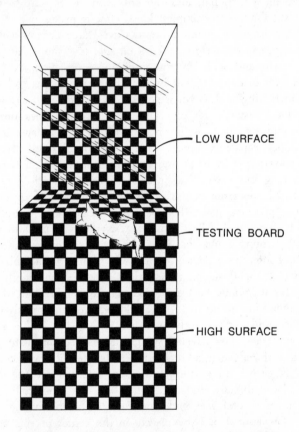

LOW SURFACE

TESTING BOARD

HIGH SURFACE

FIGURE 1.2 The "visual cliff" apparatus as it is used to test the sensory development of a puppy or other small animal. The whole apparatus is covered with a sheet of clear plate glass. The puppy is placed on a slightly raised narrow board, which apparently drops off steeply on one side and shallowly on the other. Results are based on which way the animal turns in repeated trials.

fear develops first, the time of appearance of fearful behavior on the visual cliff provides a clear-cut measure of the rapidity of sensory development. Young puppies first show this reaction at about four weeks of age, or about two weeks after their eyes open. Human infants respond as early as they can crawl, but since the test depends upon the infant's being able to move, it is not clear how much earlier than this a baby can perceive depth. Other methods for studying the development of visual perception include studies of time spent gazing at one pattern as opposed to another (in the assumption that visual preference implies an ability for visual discrimination), and studies of accommodation, or the ability to focus for distance.

Motor capacities. Behavior itself consists of movement, which can be studied in many ways. One approach is the study of movement in general as measured by activity levels, but in development we are particularly interested in the appearance of organized movement. The first organized movements of the human infant are motor reflexes such as the grasp reflex and Moro, or clasping, reflex. These reflexes appear long before organized motion of the whole body, or locomotion. The usual tests for reflex capacities are quite simple, consisting of placing the infant in various positions and observing its reaction. To give an example familiar to all parents, a baby can be held in an upright position and its attempts to stand or walk observed. Or a new-born puppy can be placed on its back and the righting reflex observed as the puppy returns to its usual posture on its stomach.

Learning capacities. These are basically capacities of the central nervous system, but their development can be inferred only through some sort of motor activity. Since learning is also dependent on the development of sensory capacities, the development of learning itself is difficult to study, and we do not have an adequate description of it even in human infants. Learning appears long before verbal responses can be made, and one objective way of studying it is to attempt to form conditioned reflexes. In the original methods developed by Pavlov (classical conditioning) the first requirement is a response which is invariably given to a stimulus. For example, a young mammal will suck on a nipple if it is placed in its mouth. Then the young animal is presented with a neutral stimulus, such as a sound that ordinarily has no effect on sucking. If the sound immediately precedes sucking on several occasions, the animal should begin to make sucking movements when it hears the sound and without the nipple's being placed in its mouth. In this form of conditioning, two kinds of stimuli become associated.

In the operant conditioning methods that Skinner developed, the association is made between the response and a stimulus which follows it. Sucking on a nipple, for example, usually produces milk, which in turn produces a pleasant taste stimulus. Sucking on a full breast or nursing bottle would therefore be rewarded or reinforced, whereas sucking on an empty breast or bottle would not, and sucking would be discontinued. If the infant is able to discriminate, before sucking, between a nipple which is always full and one which is always empty, it should give differential responses to the two and thus indicate that it is capable of learning. The operant method is probably more appropriate than the classic Pavlovian one in this case and should have wide usefulness in studying the early development of learning.

Organized behavior patterns. Sensory, motor, and learning capacities are capacities respectively of the afferent, efferent, and central portions of the nervous system, and developmental changes in organs belonging to these divisions are inferred from appropriate changes in behavior. When we study the development of behavior apart from any inferences regarding the function of the nervous system, we see that it becomes increasingly organized for adaption to changes in the external world. We can therefore speak of a fourth set of basic capacities—behavior patterns involving activity of the whole organism—and add a fourth measure of the development of behavior: the time of appearance of behavior patterns. As an example, nursing on the breast and the activity of hands, eyes, and head that goes with it is a behavior pattern. To give a general definition, a behavior pattern is a discrete piece of behavior having a special function, in this case that of obtaining milk from the breast. As an individual grows older, the behavior patterns related to eating solid foods and drinking liquids are added. Such a group of behavior patterns having a common general function may be called a behavioral system. Sucking is thus part of the ingestive behavorial system, which has the function of intake of nutritive materials, whether liquid or solid. As Table 1.1 shows, there are some nine behavorial systems into which most of the behavior of higher animals is organized. The first four of these, including ingestive behavior, shelter seeking, investi-

Table 1.1 The Major Behavioral Systems and Examples of Behavior Patterns as Observed in Dogs

System	Function	Examples of Behavior Patterns
Ingestive	Intake of nutritive substances	Gnawing, lapping
Shelter seeking (or comfort seeking)	Maintaining bodily comfort	Lying in sun; puppies lying together
Investigative	Sensory inspection of environment	Following a scent trail
Sexual	Fertilization of eggs	Mounting, clasping
Epimeletic (Care giving)	Care giving; nurturance	Licking puppies
Et-epimeletic (Care soliciting)	Calling or signaling for care	Whining, yelping
Agonistic	Adaptation to conflict	Biting, running away
Allelomimetic	Coordination of movement among individuals	Running together in a pack
Eliminative	Disposal of feces and urine	Leg lifting of males

gative behavior, and sexual behavior, are widely found in the animal kingdom and are present in some form even in one-celled animals. The last five are only found in the higher animals, particularly in vertebrates and anthropods. Care-giving behavior on the part of adults and care-soliciting behavior on the part of the young are prominent systems in the behavior of mammals and birds, as well as in that of social insects. The agonistic system, which includes behavior patterns that concern conflicts between members of the same species, is likewise found widely in the vertebrates and in many anthropods. The allelomimetic system, including patterns of behavior which have the function of coordinating movements between individuals, is only found where sense organs and environmental conditions permit precise perception of location and movements, as in flocks of birds and herds of mammals. The eliminative patterns of behavior, while highly important to civilized man, are not widely found in animals except among those which have the problem of keeping nests or lairs clean or whose eliminative behavior has taken on the secondary function of social communication. Fish, for example, show no behavior patterns associated with elimination, since the feces are carried off by water and elimination serves no function other than waste disposal.

Order of appearance of behavioral systems. In young mammals the first behavorial functions to appear are those that are essential for survival. The very first to appear in the human infant is care-soliciting, or et-epimeletic behavior, in the form of the first cry. The capacity for ingestive behavior is also present at birth, and even a suggestion of shelter-seeking behavior appears, in spite of the very poor motor development of the new-born infant.

Investigative and exploratory behaviors appear as soon as the necessary sensory and motor capacities are present. Sexual, allelomimetic, and agonistic behavior appear surprisingly early in development, but in a playful form. For example, playful sexual behavior appears in young lambs within the first ten days of life and as early as three weeks in young puppies. The last system of behavior to appear is that of care-giving behavior, which in most mammals is never seen before complete maturity and the birth of offspring.

PERIODS OF DEVELOPMENT IN THE DOG

A descriptive study of development could lead to several possible conclusions. One would be that the rate of change is uniform throughout development so that the whole process would be gradual and continuous. Another would be that the rate of development would be fast at certain times and slow at others, giving rise to discontinuity of development. As the study of almost any mammal shows, the latter hypothesis seems to be correct and on this basis development can be divided into definite periods (Scott and Fuller, 1965).

The neonatal period, birth until two weeks. Puppies are born with both eyes and ears closed and are therefore effectively both blind and deaf. They respond to taste, but the sense of smell is little developed. They are consequently highly insulated from stimulation by the external environment. Orientation to the mother and litter mates is accomplished almost entirely through the sense of touch, as puppies respond positively to warm, soft objects and negatively to pain and cold. Motor capacities are likewise limited, being restricted to crawling, sucking, and distress vocalization.

Learning capacities are, of course, limited by these deficiencies in sensory and motor abilities and in addition are slower and less efficient than adult capacities. To date, no one has been able to condition responses to painful stimulation earlier than about one week of age, and even then, responses are unstable and acquired only through many repetitions. Operant conditioning of the sucking response probably occurs earlier, but no information is available on how rapidly this occurs. In short, the new-born puppy can learn little and is extremely difficult to train.

Social behavior patterns are completely adapted to neonatal life. Ingestive behavior is limited to sucking, and eliminative behavior occurs only as a reflex in response to licking by the mother. A primitive form of investigative behavior is a slow crawl, during which the puppy throws its head from side to side. All other adaptations are achieved through care-soliciting behavior. If hungry, cold, or hurt, the puppy gives a rapid series of whines or yelps until relieved by its mother or a human caretaker.

The transition period, from two until three weeks. The first sign of change is the opening of the eyes, which usually takes two or three days, the eyes being completely open at thirteen days on the average. The retina is not completely developed at this time, but the puppy begins to respond to visual stimuli and will for the first time crawl backwards when confronted with a strange situation. By nineteen days of age, its ears are also open, and the puppy will twitch them or give a general startle reflex in response to a sudden noise.

Meanwhile, motor capacities are developing rapidly. The puppy can stand and walk and can lap its food in a clumsy fashion. By three weeks of age the first teeth have erupted and the puppy begins to chew. During the same period, a dramatic change takes place in learning capacities. Beginning at eighteen or nineteen days of age, the puppy can be conditioned to painful stimuli with the same speed and ease as an adult.

Toward the end of the period, the rudiments of adult social behavior patterns begin to appear. The puppy starts to wag its tail at the sight of people or animals at a distance, and playful fighting appears in the form of pawing and mouthing between litter mates. As the puppy becomes able to walk, it begins to eliminate outside the nest without assistance from its mother. In short, the puppy has undergone a rapid transition from behavior adapted to a neonatal existence to adult behavior patterns. From being a worm-like creature which does little but suckle, sleep, and eliminate, the puppy has been transformed into a young dog, recognizable in both form and behavior.

Period of socialization, from three until twelve weeks. A large number of changes are concentrated around three weeks of age. The most important of these is that the puppy begins to notice people and other animals at a distance and develops a rapidly increasing capacity for making social attachments. Hence this is called the period of primary socialization. The exact end of the period is more difficult to establish, but current evidence would place it between twelve and fourteen weeks of age, when puppies raised in large fields first begin to show signs of real independence by wandering far from their nest boxes.

During this period all of the sense organs are functional, but the cellular structure of the retina of the eye does not reach its adult form until approximately four weeks, at which time the puppy also begins to show a fear of heights. The alpha waves of the electroencephalogram, which are an indication of the functioning of the visual portion of the cerebral cortex, do not reach their adult pattern until eight weeks of age. We infer that the capacity for visual perception is increasing up to this point, and it is likely that other such capacities are likewise still developing.

In motor capacities the puppies first begin to be capable of coordinated movements over distances of more than a few feet by five or six weeks of age. By the end of the period they are capable of relatively rapid running, although they are still clumsy when compared with adults.

With respect to learning capacities, the overt responses of a puppy to food and pain can, after three weeks of age, be conditioned as readily as those of an adult, but its ability for associational learning is still limited by sensory and motor imperfections. Compared with overt motor patterns, rapid conditioning of autonomic responses, such as the change in heart rate, appears more slowly and is not actually present until about five weeks. By eight weeks of age the puppy has all the capacities of an adult as far as its central nervous system is concerned, and the next few weeks are ones in which the puppy is a ready learner. We have some evidence that the puppy must be introduced to the circumstances of its adult life during this period if it is to make a reasonably successful later adjustment.

It is in social behavior, however, that the most significant changes take place. During the early part of the period of socialization, the puppy's social activities are still chiefly organized around care-soliciting behavior, including the positive approaches of tail wagging

FIGURE 1.3 Puppies in the Neonatal Period (top) and Period of Socialization (bottom). The neonatal puppy has relatively little contact with the outside world, being both blind and deaf. The picture shows the typical slow crawl, swinging the head from side to side. In contrast, the puppy in the critical period is alert and sensitive to outside events.

and soliciting attention and the substitution of distress vocalization for more directly adaptive reactions to painful or uncomfortable stimulation. Distress vocalization in response to isolation in a strange place first appears just before three weeks and begins to decline at about six or seven weeks, which is also the time when the puppy is first likely to be completely weaned from the breast. As care-soliciting behavior declines, it is replaced by direct forms of social adjustment.

This is also the period in which ingestive behavior switches over to its adult form. The puppy can lap liquids and chew solid foods to some extent at the beginning of the period, but if it is well nourished, it may continue to nurse and neglect other foods until it is about four or five weeks of age. A mother begins to wean her puppies from the breast when they are about seven weeks old. By this time she is not only running out of milk, but her offspring have developed good sets of needle-sharp teeth.

These teeth play a part in the development of agonistic behavior. Growling over bones and playful fighting appear early in the period. Competition over food results in the development of a stable dominance order during the next few weeks. The capacity for escape behavior and fearful reactions also develops rapidly and becomes one of the chief limiting factors of the process of primary socialization, or the forming of the first social attachments. On the other hand, the chief behavioral mechanism for initiating positive contact is social investigation. After a brief period of fright, the young puppy investigates any new animal or person. Investigation of the anal and genital regions of another puppy is one of the first signs of sexual behavior. Brief mounting also appears during this period, but more frequently in males than females.

Shortly after the beginning of the period, at approximately three weeks of age, the puppy starts to respond to social isolation and will vocalize loudly if left alone, particularly in a strange place. Along with this reaction he shows the first signs of allelomimetic behavior. Puppies begin to follow each other's movements and to move in miniature packs over short distances. They also begin to sleep in places other than the nest box, indicating that they are now capable of seeking shelter and comfort under their own power.

Of particular interest to dog owners is the development of eliminative behavior. Soon after three weeks of age, a puppy begins to urinate and defecate by itself, usually not far from the nest box. By eight weeks of age it has begun to eliminate in special spots, preceding the act by wandering around and nosing the ground. The next few weeks are the most favorable time for house breaking, although a puppy is not capable of long periods of continence until about twelve weeks old. However, from the very start of the period, at three weeks of age, a puppy will refuse to soil its own sleeping place and will remain continent overnight if confined in it.

In short, during the period of socialization there is rapid development of all basic systems of behavior with the exception of epimeletic, or care-giving behavior, which does not appear until the animals become sexually mature and either have puppies of their own or come into contact with those of other mothers.

The most important event in this period is primary socialization, or the formation of the first emotional attachments. During the early part of the period, the puppy's typical reaction to a strange individual is a momentary startle response and then a cautious approach, wagging its tail. As a result, the puppy is likely to make contact with any strange person or animal that stays in its vicinity for any length of time. As it grows older, the initial fear responses become stronger, and its ability to run away likewise increases, so that by six or seven weeks of age a puppy raised apart from human beings in a large field will keep completely out of contact for long periods. By fourteen weeks fear and escape responses have become so strong that any puppy raised in these surroundings acts like a wild animal. This behavior effectively prevents prolonged contact with strangers and thus eliminates any opportunity of forming an attachment.

The process of attachment itself appears to be an internal emotional one which can take place as a result of relatively brief contact, even as little as a few minutes per day. The peak of the capacity for rapid socialization occurs between six and eight weeks of age.

Juvenile period, twelve weeks to sexual maturity. This is a period in which the most important process is that of achieving social independence. It starts at about twelve weeks of age with the puppy's beginning to investigate areas away from the nest, and by its end, at six months of age, the puppy has most of the capacities of an adult dog and can become an effective hunter.

Sensory and learning capacities have already been fully developed, but motor capacities continue to improve. A puppy grows very rapidly until sixteen weeks of age, when it has achieved approximately 60 percent of its adult size. Afterward it begins to grow more slowly.

Its second teeth begin to come in at sixteen weeks of age, and the puppy is soon able to bite effectively and chew hard objects like bones. Puppies raised in large fields achieve a considerable degree of running speed and motor coordination even at the start of the period, and these abilities improve markedly as the animals grow larger and stronger. There are few changes in social behavior.

Pubertal period, sexual maturity to birth of young. Sexual maturity in some breeds of dogs may take place as early as five months of age, but there is a great deal of variability among breeds and individuals. Most females will show their first heat periods before one year of age, while the development of males tends to be a little slower. In wolves sexual maturity does not occur until the spring before the animals are two or sometimes three years of age, so it is obvious that their dog descendents have been selected for sexual precocity.

With sexual maturity, dogs begin to defend their home ground as a territory by barking at strangers and making attacks on strange animals. Sexually mature animals also begin to show the adult form of eliminative behavior by marking objects during the course of their wanderings away from home. The leg-lifting reaction of males is one of the first signs of puberty, although not necessarily of readiness for mating.

Parental period, birth of young to cessation of reproduction. Successful mating is soon followed by the birth of puppies and the appearance of care-giving or epimeletic behavior on the part of the mother. In the wild canids such as the wolf, all males and females in the pack respond to the young and vomit food for them. Epimeletic behavior will not be discussed in detail here as it is not associated with early development, but a bitch can do a successful job of caring for her young puppies even though she has been hand-raised entirely apart from other dogs.

PERIODS OF DEVELOPMENT IN OTHER MAMMALS

The mammals used in experimental studies of the development of behavior belong to five important orders. Dogs, of course, belong to the order Carnivora, which includes a group of related animals whose principal food is meat. The common laboratory animals such as rats, mice, and guinea pigs all belong to the order Rodentia, or rodents. This order includes a great variety of small to medium-sized mammals,

all of which have chisel-like front teeth. Most of them live on various
sorts of vegetation rather than on meat. The large grazing animals,
or ungulates, live entirely upon plants. Many important domestic
animals, including the pig, cow, sheep, and horse, belong to this group,
which is divided into two orders: the Artiodactyla, or even-toed ungulates, and the Perissodactyla, or odd-toed forms, such as the horse.
Finally, many developmental studies are now being done on monkeys
and apes, members of the order Primata, the group to which man
himself belongs.

Carnivores. Most of these animals have the same developmental problems as dogs, arising from similar food habits. Since the
mothers cannot be inactive for long periods, the young must either
develop rapidly or remain at home while the mother hunts. Most
developmental studies other than those on dogs have been done on
domestic cats. In contrast to lions, the largest and most highly social
members of the cat family, adult domestic cats are small and almost
solitary animals. They prey consistently on small mammals and birds,
which means that there is little possibility of catching animals large
enough to be shared among a group.

Compared with the development of puppies, that of kittens is
considerably more rapid. Their eyes open more quickly, and they are already beginning to hunt for food for themselves by the time they reach
six or seven weeks of age. The mother cat brings home live prey
for her kittens and allows them to play with it, thus giving them an
opportunity to practice hunting with wounded and helpless prey.
There is more prolonged attention to the young than in dogs and
consequently more opportunity for teaching by the mother. For these
reasons, cats have been used primarily for studying the development
of the mother-offspring relationship.

Rodents. The house mouse has been domesticated chiefly
as a laboratory mammal useful in the study of genetics, being chosen
because of its short life span and great fertility. House mice are quite
small, even for rodents, and are preyed upon by many sorts of birds
and mammals. They are highly fearful and nervous animals, and most
of their behavior is adapted to escaping detection and pursuit. Mice
build nests for their young, and almost all of their social life takes
place within this small ball of fibers. They have a gestation period of
only twenty-one days, and their young are born completely hairless as
well as blind and deaf. The neonatal period is short, running through

the first four days, in which they do little but suckle on the mother. The first change takes place on the fifth day when their hair begins to grow; a transition period then follows and continues through the twelfth day. Unlike the dog, the ears become functional before the eyes; the opening of the eye thus marks the end of the transition period rather than the beginning. The period of socialization runs from twelve through twenty-five days of age, ending with final weaning, but the major processes of attachment take place prior to eighteen or nineteen days. Fear responses which prevent close contact with strange animals are developed during this time, and at its end the young mice must leave the nest to find their own food. The peculiarities of mouse development are its rapid course and the fact that most of it takes place within a very limited area—the nest and its immediate surroundings (Williams and Scott, 1953).

The Norway rat is also a domesticated laboratory rodent, but it should not be considered as simply a large mouse. Adult rats are much less vulnerable to predators than mice and have many more social contacts outside the nest. For example, one of the behavior patterns of wild rats is to carry food and store it in various secluded places where it becomes available to all rats.

Like mice, rats are born naked and helpless with both eyes and ears closed. They go through a short neonatal period in which behavior is chiefly expressed as nursing, squealing, and sleeping. The first changes in behavior are the appearance of self-grooming, and the face-washing pattern first becomes functional on day 5 (Bolles and Woods, 1964). Since this is an adult pattern of behavior, we may consider day 5 as the beginning of the transition period.

The major senses appear in the same order as in mice but somewhat later. The startle response to sound appears on day 13 instead of day 11, while the eyes begin to open on day 14 instead of day 12 and ordinarily are not completely open until about day 17.

The transition from infantile to adult locomotion takes place between ten and seventeen days, beginning with standing and walking and ending with the slow, controlled walk of the adult about day 17. The transition to the adult forms of eating and drinking occur about day 16 when the young rat will first hold and nibble a food pellet as well as begin to drink water from a fount.

The earliest form of social behavior, grooming other animals, appears about day 13. Several days after this, playful fighting appears as a separate form of activity, on about the twentieth day.

On the basis of this information we can say that the major transitions occur between days 5 and 17, with the most pronounced changes taking place between ten and seventeen days. Most changes occur from two to four days later in the rat than in the mouse. No data are available on the period of socialization in rats. Most laboratory rats are arbitrarily weaned at the age of twenty-one days, which is before the mothers have ceased to nurse their young and clean up their feces. Thus almost all laboratory rats are early weaned animals. Observation indicates that some emotional disturbance occurs at separation, and it is possible that much behavior that is considered "normal" is based on animals subjected to emotional shock and curtailed maternal contacts in early life.

The development of wild rats indicates that complete maturity in the behavorial sense does not occur until about ninety days. Thus a juvenile period of at least two months follows the time when the socialization period ends.

Another rodent, the guinea pig, is highly precocious. There is a long period of gestation, some sixty-eight days, and the young are born as miniature adults with all their sensory capacities present. They are able to run about at birth and even nibble on solid food. It is difficult to wean a young guinea pig from the breast until it is three or four days of age, but otherwise there is very little further behavorial development until sexual maturity.

Ungulates. Most of the hoofed mammals live in large herds, sometimes including hundreds or thousands of individuals. The herds must keep moving from place to place in order to find enough grass, and the young must stick close to their mothers if they are to survive. Consequently, the mother-offspring relationship is a highly important one. Sheep and goat mothers become attached only to their own offspring, rejecting all others, and the attachment is formed within a few hours after birth. This means that the young lamb or kid can suckle only from its own mother and must remain constantly nearby even in the largest herds. The same phenomenon probably takes place in other herd animals but has not been established experimentally.

All ungulates are precocious in behavioral development. To take the sheep as an example (Scott, 1945), the young lamb is born in a highly mature state and is able to follow its mother within a few hours after birth. It begins to nibble on grass at about ten days of age but continues to nurse throughout the first summer, at the end of which it has almost reached mature size. The lamb forms its social attach-

ment to the mother within the first few days after birth. We can therefore conclude that the first ten days comprise both a neonatal period,
in that it is concerned with the process of nursing, and also the period
of primary socialization. There is almost no transition period, since
most adult sensory and motor capacities are present shortly after birth.

The domestic goat is different from the sheep in that the
mothers often leave their offspring for long periods during the first
two weeks of life. The kid remains motionless while she is away, and
an observer can approach within a few feet and sometimes even touch
it before it runs away. The same "freezing" behavior is seen in many
members of the deer family, and "abandoned" fawns are often picked
up and bottle reared by persons who are ignorant of this behavior.

Primates. This order, which includes man and his close biological relatives, includes a great variety of animals, of which the
Anthropoidea, or great apes, are closest to the human species. Behavorial
development differs considerably, but all primates have certain things
in common. The major sense organs are functional at birth, both eyes
and ears being open. Among the general characteristics of primate
development is a long nursing period, during which the mothers make
little or no effort to feed their young solid food. As with ungulates,
the general rule is that only one baby is born at a time, and is nursed
only by its own mother. However, other adults may be interested in
the baby, and adoptions sometimes take place if a mother dies. Primates
have long periods of gestation, are relatively large when born, and
grow relatively slowly as young animals.

Jay's (1963) report on the Indian Langur monkey is one of the
few detailed developmental studies of wild primates. When first born,
the baby monkey is the object of great interest among the adult females, and the mother allows it to be passed from hand to hand. Its
own behavior is adapted to life in its mother's arms, and the most
obvious behavior patterns are those of nursing and clinging to the
mother. Motor development is quite rapid. By two weeks of age, the
infant may climb on its mother's body, and by a month it may move
as far away as three to five feet. The infant continues to interact
almost entirely with its mother until it is approximately three months
old. Then a transition period begins, during which the infant first begins to eat solid food and to climb on bushes and trees as well as on its
mother's body. She and other mothers begin to leave their infants for
short stretches of time during which the young begin to play with

each other. At the same time the color of the infants' fur changes from dark brown to gray, with the result that they no longer have a color distinct from that of adults. Coinciding with this change, adults become much less interested in the young animals. From five to twelve months, the infant plays several hours a day with others of its own age but still returns to its mother for nursing. Between eleven to fifteen months, the mother gradually weans her infant and finally refuses to let it either nurse or cling to her body. Thus, the juvenile period begins when the young monkey is approximately fifteen months old. There is no evidence as to the age at which primary socialization begins, but judging from the general rate of maturation in this species, it must take place while the infant is still being carried in its mother's arms.

The development of rhesus monkeys appears to be quite similar except that this species lives on the ground more than do langurs. Newborn infants consistently cling to the mothers and, as Harlow's (1965) studies show, a baby separated from its mother will not survive unless it is supplied with some object to which it can cling. Experimental evidence shows that learning capacities develop quite rapidly, and at least some are present within the first few days.

Chimpanzees are more closely related to human beings, and their development is correspondingly more similar to human development than is that of monkeys. Like the langurs, newborn chimpanzees cling to their mothers and are carried by them from three to six months. Unlike rhesus monkeys, young chimpanzees can be reared without objects to which they can cling, and they can be cared for in very much the same fashion as human babies. Like the langurs, they are able to walk and climb independently between three and five months. Their nursing period is even longer, some being weaned as late as two years of age, at least in captivity. Compared with our information on human development, relatively little is known about these rare animals. Changes in motor development and physical maturation take place more rapidly than in human infants (at about half the corresponding ages) but in much the same sequence.

From this brief review of mammalian infancy we can see that there is much variation in the occurrence of periods of development. In some species the periods are much more definite than in others. Both the total lengths of development and the relative length of periods can vary a great deal. These conclusions, however, are based on small amounts of information, and a very different picture may emerge when more species have been thoroughly studied.

PERIODS OF DEVELOPMENT
IN BIRDS

A great many experiments on early experience have been done with young birds. These are, of course, very different sorts of animals from mammals, being adapted primarily for life in the air. One characteristic of all birds, however, is rapid development. Even the largest birds reach adult size within a period of several weeks. This means that birds never experience the lengthy period of training, exploration, and informal learning that occurs prior to adult life in many mammals. However, as with mammals at birth, there is a great deal of variation in the state of development of birds at hatching. They are customarily grouped either as *precocial*, those capable of self feeding at hatching, and generally including heavy-bodied birds which live most of their lives upon land or water or as *altricial*, parent-fed birds hatched in an immature state, and usually including excellent flyers which spend much of their lives in the air.

Development of altricial birds. The word altricial means nourishing, and altricial birds are those which feed their young. A well-studied example is the song sparrow, a bird which goes through its entire early development within thirty days (Nice, 1943). The young birds are hatched with a sparse covering of down, and their early behavior is concerned almost entirely with nutrition. Any disturbance of the nest is likely to produce gaping reactions, which enable the parent birds to stuff food into their mouths. This nestling stage is very similar to the neonatal stage of such slow-developing mammals as dogs and mice.

The first sign in a young song sparrow of a transition to adult capacities appears at five to six days when its eyes first open. Primary socialization begins at seven to nine days when the first fear reactions are shown. At ten to sixteen days the feathers appear, and the young bird can be called a fledgling; at the same time, it leaves the nest for its first flight. By twenty-eight days of age, the young song sparrow is almost as large as an adult and is capable of full flight. The juvenile song sparrow is much like the adult except for a different coloring of its feathers. Thus the periods of development in this altricial bird are very similar to those in the dog but are passed through much more rapidly. (See Table 1.2).

Table 1.2 Periods and Processes of Development in the Song Sparrow*

Periods Described by Nice	Length of Period (Days)	Major Developmental Processes	Initial Changes
Stage 1 (nestling)	0–4	Feeding by parents	Hatching, gaping
Stage 2 (nestling)	5–6	Transition to adult sensory capacities	Eyes open
Stage 3 (nestling)	7–9	Formation of primary social relationships (imprinting) (also in stages 4, 5)	Cowering, first fear reactions
Stage 4 (fledgling)	10–16	Transition to adult motor capacities (also in stage 5)	Leaving nest, first flight
Stage 5 (fledgling)	17–28		Full flight
Stage 6 (juvenile)	29–50	Like adult except for plumage and reproduction	Independent feeding

* Note that the first stage is much like the neonatal stage in the puppy but that the processes of primary socialization and transition to adult sensory and motor activities overlap each other to a greater extent.

Another altricial bird, the jackdaw, which belongs to the crow family, has been used by Lorenz (1935) in many experiments with early experience. Still another altricial bird, the pigeon, is interesting in that it feeds its young with a secretion from the crop, called crop milk, and in this respect is somewhat similar to mammals.

Precocial birds. The species most commonly studied developmentally are chickens and ducks. Baby chicks are hatched with a complete coat of down but lack feathers. They are not fed by the mothers but must begin to pick up their own food within the first twenty-four hours of life. The chicks emerge from the egg with all the sense organs functional and are capable of walking at hatching. Imprinting, as primary socialization is usually called in birds, takes place within the first twenty-four hours. Transition to the adult form of locomotion depends upon the development of feathers and the consequent ability to fly. Locomotor transition takes somewhat longer than in the song sparrow since chickens are larger birds, but they are usually completely feathered and are approaching adult size by six weeks of age. Ducks are hatched in a similar state of maturity except that they are also able to swim. As with chickens, the period of primary socialization is very short, extending over a few hours during the first day. Bodily growth and the development of feathers are, if anything, more rapid than with chickens.

In conjunction with their short and rapid development, the social behavior patterns of birds are usually more stereotyped than those of mammals and also less susceptible to modification by training and experience.

Periods and processes. From these comparisons we can see that the major periods of development are somewhat arbitrary in length but are important in that they serve to indicate times at which significant developmental processes take place. Such processes may be confined to different periods, as they are in the development of the dog and other mammals born in an immature state, or they may greatly overlap each other, as they do in precocious mammals like the sheep. The essential processes are those of neonatal nutrition or suckling, transition to the adult forms of locomotion and ingestive behavior, and the formation of primary social relationships. As we have seen, there are tremendous differences between species with respect to the duration of these processes, the order in which they appear after birth, and the degree of overlap. We should always remember that named periods of development are useful because they are essentially a convenient and practical way of designating and memorizing the times at which various processes are proceeding most actively.

THE EVOLUTION OF BEHAVIORAL DEVELOPMENT

Ecology and behavioral development. The behavioral development of the domestic dog is most understandable through a study of its wild ancestors, the wolves. These animals are primarily hunters of the large herd animals: moose, caribou, deer, or mountain sheep; although in emergencies they can live on animals as small as mice and eat a variety of other food, including berries, bones, and carrion. They usually hunt in packs, and the prey is shared by the whole group.

Reproduction in the wolf and in its tame descendent, the dog, is adapted to this sort of existence. The gestation period is quite short, some sixty-three days, and the weight of the unborn puppies becomes an added burden to the mother only in the latter half of pregnancy. The puppies are born in an extremely immature state, and the mother cares for them constantly during the first two or three weeks. After this time, she leaves the puppies to hunt and returns to feed them only once or twice a day by vomiting food and by nursing. When the puppies are about seven weeks of age she weans them from the breast and thereafter is completely unhampered in her activity. The puppies grow very rapidly until four months of age, being fed both by their own mother and other members of the pack. By six months of age, they are capable of hunting on their own. The whole reproductive process is adjusted so as to provide the minimum of interference with hunting. One result is that, even without the aid of a pack, a pregnant female has a good chance of rearing a litter on her own. The brief and limited contact between the canine mother and offspring is very different from the situation in human beings and most primate societies, and also from that in herd animals, whose young are born ready to follow the mother, but the wolf's relatively long period of dependence makes development similar to that of human beings.

The above example indicates that behavioral development is related to ecology; that is, the mode of development is adapted to the general living habits of a species, its position in a food chain, and its relations to other members of an animal community. To take another instance, the sheep occupies the general ecological niche of a plant-eating animal. Sheep obtain their food by grazing from place to place, and their wild ancestors have no fixed spot in which they sleep or live. Mountain sheep live in or near rocky cliffs, where they are relatively safe from their chief predators, wolves. Behavioral development is quite rapid, and these animals are most vulnerable to predators when quite young. Within a few days a young lamb can run and climb very nearly as well as the adults. Along with this precocity sheep have a long gestation period of approximately five months, and ordinarily only one lamb is born at a time. Such precocious development is found in all the herd animals, and single births are the rule in most of them. One exception is the pig, which combines precocious development with multiple births. Pigs are also somewhat unusual ungulates in that they are omnivorous, with the result that their diet includes more concentrated foods than those eaten by most grazing animals.

Many rodents provide other examples of herbivorous mammals which are the prey of other species. These smaller animals often eat concentrated food such as seeds and nuts, and in any case, the amount of food eaten does not require very wide movements to obtain it. Many rodents therefore live in limited areas and protect themselves and their young from predators by building nests in burrows. Large litters of young are born in a highly immature state, adapted only for living in a protected environment. An exception is the guinea pig, which produces small litters of precocious young. As far as is known, their wild ancestors do not build nests or burrows but live in rocky crevices, the young finding protection by following their mothers into these natural shelters.

Primates show a great deal of variability in their ecological relationships. Some are as small as squirrels and look a great deal like them. At the opposite end of the scale are the large, human-appearing anthropoid apes. Most primates are omnivorous, but some, like gorillas, are almost completely herbivorous. The smaller primates are preyed upon by carnivores, and the larger ones, such as baboons and chimpanzees, may occasionally prey on smaller mammals. Many primates spend most of their lives in trees, others spend part of their lives on the ground as do the great apes, and a few are plains living, like the baboons and man. All of them have the habit of bearing one young at a time, and, except for the great apes and man, most of them are born in a precocious state with respect to locomotion. Among primates, size seems to be more important here than ecology in relation to precocity of development.

In short, the developmental pattern of a species has some relationship to its general ecology, but there are no universal rules about it. In birds, behavioral development is strongly related to the aerial life of these animals, being characterized by extremely rapid post-hatching development directed toward achieving flying as soon as possible. In general, the tree-nesting and flying birds are altricial. Nevertheless, many special adaptions are possible. Wood ducks are precocial but nest in trees from which the young have to jump before they can fly, and the ground-nesting gulls and terns have altricial young which can survive because nesting always takes place on small islands where predators do not come. There are many alternate ways in which an animal can adapt to a given environment, and the development of behavior is no exception.

Adaption to the neonatal and adult social environment. Birds, as we have pointed out earlier, are often classified as being either precocial (hatched in a relatively mature state) or altricial (hatched in an immature state that necessitates feeding by the parents). The same sort of classification can be made for mammals, with the exception that all mammals are altricial in the sense that all are first fed by their mothers through suckling. One might expect that such a simple classification into two categories would be arbitrary and that there would be many cases in which animals would be only partially precocial with a consequent overlap between the categories. Such is certainly the case in mammals. Primates are much more precocious in the development of their sense organs than are rats or dogs, and among primates the monkeys are much more precocious in locomotion than are the great apes or man. The evolutionary factor determining precocity appears to be the kind of early social environment to which behavioral adaptation is made.

Precocity can be understood if we assume two tendencies in the evolution of social behavior. The first is toward the parents providing a highly protected existence for the newborn young, and the second is toward a different and mutually protecting existence for adults. Consequently, behavioral development in an animal like the dog should be related to two social environments, the first being that provided by parental care and the second consisting of interaction with adults. Evolutionary selection for the development of adaptive behavior should therefore proceed in two directions. This contrasts with the situation in animals like sheep, where parental care is minimal, and individuals live within the herd from birth until death, with relatively slight changes in the social environment. One important consequence of this idea is that it implies that behavior which is adapted for the neonatal existence may not necessarily lead into behavior adapted to the adult existence. In short, certain kinds of early behavior may have little significance for later development except that they insure the immediate survival of the individual.

Social organization and behavioral development. The social environment into which a young animal is born depends to a large extent upon the social organization characteristic of its species. For example, the most important and long lasting social group in small rodents such as house mice and deer mice is that of the mother and young litter living in a nest. As adults, mice go out to feed in a solitary fashion and may not come into contact with each other more than once or twice a day. When they do meet, the usual reaction is mutual avoidance, although sexual behavior may result if a female in estrus meets a male.

Almost the entire early development of these animals takes place within the nest, including the maturation of the sensory and motor organs and the process of socialization. This correlates with the fact that the social organization of adults, either as mothers with litters or as parts of a "sleeping aggregation," also takes place in the nest.

By contrast, the large herd animals have no nests and under natural conditions spend their entire lives in the open. Wild mountain sheep have separate male and female herds during the time when the young are born. Since the lambs are all born at the same season, primary socialization takes place to the mothers and to a peer group of the same age. Adult males and females only come together during the autumn breeding season.

Domestic herds are managed in somewhat the same fashion, the females ordinarily being kept apart from the males in order to control the season of birth. Under these conditions, a strong leader-follower relationship develops between mother and offspring, and the young lambs generalize this relationship to all older sheep.

In most respects domestic goats have a similar social organization to that of sheep except that leader-follower relationships are much weaker. This latter fact is correlated with a difference in early development. Young lambs constantly follow their mothers from birth, but young kids are usually left by their mothers while the latter go off to graze, the kids showing characteristic "freezing" behavior while alone. (The same sort of behavior can be seen in young fawns belonging to wild deer.) Young lambs therefore get much more practice in following their mothers during early life than do young kids, and this persists in adult life as a difference in leader-follower relationships.

A still more striking instance of the relationship between early development and adult social organization is found in dogs and wolves. For the first two or three weeks of life, the mothers are highly attentive to their offspring and in some cases will leave them for only a few minutes out of the entire twenty-four hours. When the young are about three weeks of age, their mothers begin to stay away from them for long periods. In the case of wolves, the mother spends this time in hunting and may see her offspring no more than once or twice in twenty-four hours. During the same period, the young puppy or wolf cub is going through the period of socialization. This means that he has the opportunity to form his strongest social relationships with his litter mates, who are constantly with him, rather than with his parents or other adult animals. Such early experience forms the foundation of the typical adult social group, or pack, composed of peers rather than parents and offspring.

Primate societies take still other forms. In the baboon (DeVore, 1963), the social group is composed of males, females, and offspring in all stages of development. In the center of the troop is a large dominant male. Other males spread out around him, keeping their distance from him and from each other. Close to the dominant male in the center of the group are females with young infants, with other females somewhat further away. There is no permanent consortship between males and females, and consequently no social structure which resembles a human nuclear family of male, female, and their offspring. On the other hand, the offspring of a particular female tend to stay near her and to associate with each other.

The young infant stays with its mother constantly for many weeks after birth and only cautiously begins to take small journeys away from her to associate with other young animals. Here the first opportunity for socialization is with an older animal, the mother, and one characteristic of baboon societies is the permanent association of younger and older individuals.

We can conclude that the course of behavioral development is strongly related to the social organization typical of the species. Not only does social organization form one of the most important parts of the environment into which a young animal is born, but the course of development itself foreshadows and partially determines future social relationships into which the young animal may enter. It follows that if the behavorial development of a young animal is disturbed by any means this will have an effect upon its future capacity to enter into social organization. It also follows that if the social organization of a group is altered or upset, any animal whose development has followed the usual course will be maladjusted.

SUMMARY

As we have seen in this short survey of various species of mammals and birds, the course of development can differ widely in different kinds of animals. Consequently, the same sort of experimental variable can give very different results when applied to a different species and must be interpreted in a different fashion. We can only draw conclusions from an animal experiment and apply them to human development in situations where we have a firm knowledge of development of behavior in both-species.

Duration of development. The behavioral development of some animals is a matter of days, as in the song birds, or it may extend over many years as it does in man and some other primates. Such wide variation means that rapidly developing animals cannot have the same sorts of early experience as the slower ones, particularly with regard to learning, training, and habit formation. One simply cannot expose a young chicken or duck, or even a mouse, to the same length of experience as is possible with the more slowly developing mammals.

Maturity at birth or hatching. Animals also differ a great deal in respect to the degree of maturity at which they are born or hatched. It is therefore impossible for an experimenter to give a newborn lamb or guinea pig the same type of experience that he gives to an immature puppy or mouse. Birds and mammals are often classified as precocious or non-precocious, but in fact there are all degrees of precocity and a wide variety of ways in which an animal can be advanced or retarded.

Order of developmental events. The times of appearance of sensory, motor, and learning capacities serve as useful developmental landmarks for making comparisons between species. Similarly, the time of origin of organized behavior patterns provides a useful means of comparing development in species which are closely enough related so that similar behavior patterns are recognizable. A comparison of these developmental landmarks in different species shows that they actually may appear in different sequence. There is no simple scheme of behavorial development that can be applied to all animals.

Periods of development. The behavioral development of all animals can be divided into periods based upon the occurrence of major developmental processes. This emphasizes the fact that development is itself a dynamic process, or rather a group of processes which wax and wane as time goes on. It follows that processes can be most easily modified when they are at points of maximum activity, as a process only exists while it is active.

The evolution of behavioral development. In different animals, behavioral development has evolved in different ways, each adapted to the biological and physical environments in which the particular species ordinarily lives. Behavioral development is also importantly related to the social environment, which in a highly social species is likely to be the most stable part of its surroundings. In animals which are born or hatched in an immature state, evolution of development has proceeded toward adaptation to two different aspects of social environment. In early development, all behavior may be adapted to a kind of existence in which nutrition and a high degree of care are provided by the parent animals. In later life, behavior is adapted to a more independent existence, part of which involves the adults' providing the sort of care which the young animal receives. There must be a transition period between the two sorts of existence, and there is an implication that behavior in the earlier period may be significant only during that period and may not directly develop into adult behavior.

The results of comparative developmental psychology throw a great deal of light on developmental processes, as well as on the nature of human development. However, only a very few animal species have been studied in any detail, and we can predict that future systematic studies will produce many new facts and hypotheses. The comparative study of development is a mine of information whose surface has barely been scratched.

2 PERIODS AND PROCESSES OF EARLY HUMAN DEVELOPMENT

As we have seen in the previous chapter, mammals and birds have a tendency to evolve dual forms of behavioral development, one directed toward adaptation for a situation in which adults provide food and care, and the other toward adaptation for a more independent adult existence. The result is that many animals have a distinct early period in which all behavior is adapted to the neonatal existence. This evolutionary tendency toward separation and specialization of infantile and adult behavior varies with the degree of parental care found in a species. Early human development is adapted to a kind of parental care which is as complete as that found in any lower animal, and whose duration greatly exceeds any other known instance.

Bearing in mind that periods of development are always somewhat arbitrary, that they represent times at which certain processes are proceeding more rapidly than others, and that there may be a great deal of variation in the speed of development, let us examine human development for evidence of the existence of natural periods.

THE NEONATAL PERIOD

The major process of the neonatal period is the infantile form of ingestive behavior and the resulting nutrition and growth. Like any other mammal, the human newborn infant is capable of suckling and receives most of its nourishment through milk. With considerable help it can also drink from a cup or an eye dropper, but under no circumstances can it either feed itself with solid food or chew and swallow such food if someone attempts to feed it.

Sensory development. A baby's sensory capacities are well developed at birth, in that some response can be elicited by stimulation through all the major sense organs. Newborn infants give a startle response to sound and respond in various ways to tactile stimuli. They also give a startle response to strong odors such as anise and asafoetida. Lipsitt (1966) has shown that the human neonate will adapt, or accommodate, to one of these odors just as adults will, and soon stops responding. If a second odor is then presented, the startle response reappears in full strength. This reaction shows that the neonate can differentiate between odors. Eisenberg and her co-workers (1964) have shown that differential responses are given to different auditory signals, indicating that the neonate can also differentiate sounds.

Visual capacities can be studied in a variety of ways. Neonatal infants react to sudden changes in light intensity with pupillary and eye-closing reflexes and even by bending the head backward. They respond to a change in the position of an object by following it with their eyes. However, one of the responses best adapted to the study of developmental changes is that of fixating on stationary objects. As Fantz (1965) has shown, the time spent looking at any new object is quite short at birth and greatly increases between one and a half and two months of age.

The alpha waves in the human electroencephalogram, which are associated with visual attention in an adult, are almost entirely absent in the neonate. They make their first appearance between two and a half and three months and are well established by four months. Taken with the behavioral evidence, this indicates that vision is poorly developed in the neonate, remains on approximately the same level for the first one and a half months, and then begins to improve rapidly over the next two and a half months.

Motor development. Motor development proceeds much more slowly than that of sensory capacities, and human infants are born more immature in this respect than almost any other higher mammal. They are completely incapable of any form of locomotion and can only move their arms and legs in a weak and uncoordinated fashion. Most infants cannot even turn over, and merely turning the head is one of their major motor capacities.

Learning. Learning capacities are likewise limited. No satisfactory demonstration of conditioning with the use of electric shock, either by classical or operant methods, has yet been made. There is some evidence that sucking can be conditioned by the use of reinforcement techniques, but whether or not this occurs as readily as with older infants has not been demonstrated (Lipsitt, 1967). Most of the evidence shows that human infants begin to be capable of rapid stable conditioning at around five weeks of age.

In one recent experiment Papousek (1967) conditioned babies to turn their heads at the sound of a buzzer by rewarding them with the opportunity to suck from a bottle. The criterion for success was turning the head in the right direction for five successive times. Newborn infants averaged 177 trials before success was achieved, three month old babies forty-two trials and a five month old group, twenty-eight trials. Since a run of five turns in one direction would be expected by pure chance in one out of thirty-two such runs, it would be expected that one chance successful run would occur in every 160 trials. Thus the newborn babies were a little slower than would be expected by pure chance, while the older ones were much faster. Whatever the explanation, the evidence shows that a baby's learning capacity improves tremendously during the first three months after birth.

On the other hand, Lipsitt's (1967) experiments with head turning show that newborn babies are capable of at least some learning. In a group of babies whose behavior was reinforced, positive responses occurred about two and a half times as often as in a group of control babies by the time both groups had experienced thirty trials, although the first group still did not respond to reinforcement in the uniform way characteristic of older infants.

It is hoped that more evidence will soon become available concerning the exact capacities for learning in infants. Evidence of change in the same individual is particularly badly needed, as most studies have been done only with newborn infants alone or with small samples of other children at random ages. Even if the capacities of the central nervous system were well developed, it is obvious that the neonatal infant is greatly limited in its total learning capacities because of limited sensory and motor abilities.

Social behavior patterns. Patterns of social behavior are likewise limited in the human neonate. Besides the infantile form of ingestive behavior, suckling, the other system of behavior which is represented is care-soliciting (et-epimeletic) behavior in the form of crying. This behavior pattern appears at birth and is the standard response to any form of physical discomfort, including hunger, cold, and pain. Elimination takes place, but no external patterns of behavior are associated with it. Unlike the newborn puppy, the infant has no control over urination or defecation.

We may therefore conclude that there is a true neonatal period in the human infant characterized by the process of neonatal nutrition. No other major developmental processes are evident, although certain kinds of transitions begin to appear at five weeks and, later, at two and a half months. By the most conservative estimates, the neonatal period covers the first month and possibly the first five or six weeks of life after birth.

PERIOD OF SOCIALIZATION

The first major change in a baby's overt behavior is the appearance of the social smile at approximately five or six weeks of age. Spitz and Wolf (1946) first demonstrated that smiling could be regularly elicited at this time by the sight of a human face or even of a mask resembling a face. Before this age, an infant may give fleeting smiles but not in response to visual stimulation.

The social smile is a very important form of human social behavior, persisting throughout life and having the general function

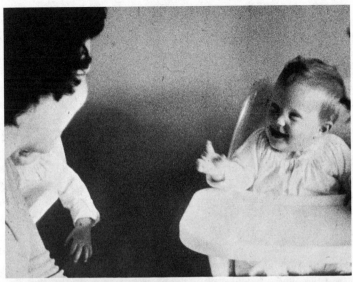

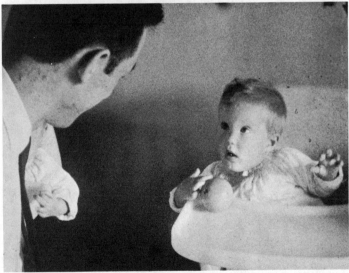

FIGURE 2.1   Social smiling in the human infant. The photographs show a typical response of a 7-month-old girl to her mother (top) and a stranger (bottom). (Enlargements from motion picture frames by D. G. Freedman.)

of a signal indicating a friendly attitude. Spitz and Wolf found that the rate of smiling at strange faces by orphanage babies increased up to five months of age, but by six months the rate had dropped almost to zero, although the babies continued to smile at familiar faces. It is obvious that they were beginning to discriminate between familiar and unfamiliar faces. After six months of age, an increasing number of babies show fear responses and cry in the presence of strangers.

Ambrose (1961) later repeated the Spitz and Wolf studies, using standardized techniques and a greater variety of subjects, and came to much the same conclusions. He further discovered that home-reared infants begin to smile at their mothers about a week earlier than the age at which orphanage babies smile for the first time at a human face. Home-reared infants also begin to discriminate against strangers earlier than do babies raised in orphanages.

In his studies of smiling in twins, Freedman (1965) found greater concordance between identical than between fraternal twins in the time when social smiling begins; thus heredity as well as the social environment affects the rate of development of this response. He also found considerable variation among unrelated children with respect to the time when the fear response to strangers first appears. In some infants this response occurs three or four months later than in others.

Thus from six weeks through approximately six months of age it is easy to make positive social contacts with infants. Indeed, the infant itself is able to make contact with strangers at a distance through the smiling response. All the evidence indicates that during this period babies become attached to certain individuals and that by its end they begin to discriminate against strangers. We can therefore call it the period of primary socialization.

A landmark for establishing the end of this period is given by Schaffer's (1958) studies of children taken to hospitals and later returned home. All infants showed some emotional disturbance, but those younger than seven months of age kept scanning the physical environment over and over again, as if attempting to recognize it, while those older than seven months showed overdependency, consisting of excessive crying when left alone, continued clinging to the mother, an increased fear of strangers, and even fear of familiar individuals within the family. We can therefore place the end of the period of socialization at the approximate average age of seven months, with considerable individual variation.

PERIODS OF TRANSITION

The transition to adult sensory capacities has relatively little importance in human infants compared with that in other animals in which some of the sense organs are completely non-functional at birth. However, some transition does occur in visual capacities at about two and a half months of age. This change overlaps with the process of socialization and, indeed, is intimately related to the development of the infant's capacity to discriminate between faces.

Similarly, the transition to the adult capacity for making rapid associations occurs toward the early part of the period when the process of socialization appears. Again, this transition may be basically necessary for socialization to take place.

Because of civilized methods of baby feeding and new methods of preparing foods that can be eaten at extremely early ages, it is very difficult to ascertain when the transition to adult forms of ingestive behavior actually begins and ends. The best evidence comes from figures on the eruption of teeth, since a baby is unable to deal efficiently with solid food without them and also because teeth tend to interfere with nursing if the baby chooses to bite. The median time for the eruption of the first tooth is approximately seven and a half months, when the front incisors begin to come in. Other teeth follow, and the first molar teeth appear at a median age of fifteen and a half months. These being grinding teeth, the baby is then first able to chew food with reasonable efficiency.

The transition to the adult form of locomotion covers the same period. The median age of crawling is seven and a half months; creeping eleven months; and walking, fifteen months. This transition, also, may be related to the process of socialization, as the baby begins to show fear of strangers at the same time that he becomes capable of moving away from them. We can conclude that the major transition processes occur between seven and a half and fifteen months of age on the average, and can therefore call this the transition period. Unlike the corresponding period in the dog, whose sensory and motor transitions occur together, the human transition period chiefly involves motor capacities.

Moreover, a type of transition which is unknown in lower animals occurs in human beings: that of transition to the adult form of communication. Before talking begins, the infant communicates by crying, babbling, and various other emotional sounds, as well as through such visual signals as smiling and arm waving. The median time that the first word is spoken is about fifteen months of age. By twenty-seven months, the baby is beginning to use more than two words at a time, is starting to speak in short sentences, and is presumably also able to understand simple sentences. We can therefore call the period from fifteen to twenty-seven months a second period of transition to the adult form of communication.

Following this transition, there begins a long period of verbal socialization, in which social relationships begin to be developed and modified through verbal communication. We could also call this the beginning of a juvenile period, corresponding to the time in lower animals which is devoted to bodily growth and the perfection of adult motor skills prior to the onset of sexual maturity.

GENERAL CONCLUSIONS

Validity of comparison of human development with that of other animals. As we have seen, each species of animals has a unique heredity and course of development. Consequently, there is no justification for assuming that the results of any experiment done on a different species can be carried over directly to human behavior. Any such transference must always be hypothetical, but the soundness of such a hypothesis can be greatly increased by basing the comparison upon fundamental resemblances between human development and that of the experimental animal concerned. The final test of the hypothesis must always be based upon facts and experiments obtained directly from human development. Without basic developmental information which allows exact comparisons, hypotheses obtained from animal work are no more than interesting suggestions that may or may not have some application to human affairs.

Relatively slow speed of human development. In one respect, human development is entirely different from that of any of the animals on which we have detailed information. The periods of human development are measured in months instead of in weeks as with dogs, in days as with rodents, or even in hours for some of the rapidly developing birds. It follows that a human infant is exposed to much more experience within a corresponding period of development, resulting in much stronger fixation of behavior by habit formation. In fact, every aspect of behavior affected by learning can be modified more strongly in human infants than in more rapidly developing animals.

This same extended experience makes much more individual variability possible in human development. Wide variation is particularly obvious in such features as motor development. The total recorded range in walking extends from eight to eighteen months, or approximately ten months difference, in children who eventually are able to walk at all. While the normal range of variation in development does not appear to be as great in the case of sensory and learning capacities as with motor capacities, there is probably at least several weeks variation in the appearance of sensory and learning abilities in reasonably normal infants. Consequently, any interpretation of experimental results based on age from birth must always allow for variation. For example, an experiment based on the conclusion that the median time for the beginning of the motor transition period is seven months would always be affected by the fact that half of the infants of this particular age would still be in the earlier period. It would therefore be safer to choose children for comparison who were several months apart in development so that relatively little overlap would be expected. Similarly, any description of populations based on change in behavior with age would show less abrupt changes than would be seen in the individuals themselves. For example, when a child begins to walk, the change is quite sudden and abrupt, often taking place within a few days. Yet a statistical study of a population would show a gradual change taking place over a period of several months. It is well to remember that development actually takes place in individuals rather than on a population basis.

Unusual features of human development. Philosophers and scientists in the past have often tried to demonstrate that human beings are at least in some ways completely different from other animals. As we have learned more and more about animal behavior, this has become increasingly difficult, since we can find at least the rudiments of almost any human activity elsewhere in the animal kingdom. For example, human development is in many ways quite similar to that of dogs. In both species there is an early neonatal period in which behavior has evolved toward adaptation to complete maternal care, as opposed to later periods of development in which adaptation is based on adult forms of behavior with increasing independence. The same fundamental general processes of development can be observed in both, and these can be used to identify the same general periods of development. However, the human infant seems to have an unusual combination of somewhat precocious development of the sense organs and relatively delayed development of the motor capacities. In contrast, rhesus monkeys are highly precocious in learning and motor skills, and even chimpanzees, which are perhaps most similar to human beings in general development, show much more rapid changes in motor capacities than do human infants. It should be emphasized that we still do not have a thorough description of the fundamental facts of development of any primate species other than man, and these conclusions may be modified by future discoveries.

Table 2.1 Periods and Processes in Early Human Development

Period	Approximate Age Limits	Major Processes	Initial Changes
Neonatal	0–5 weeks	Establishment of neonatal nutrition (sucking)	Birth
Primary socialization	5 weeks–7 months	Formation of primary social relationships and emotional attachments	First social smiling
Transition 1	7–15 months	Transition to adult methods of eating and locomotion	Change in response to separation; first tooth; crawling
Transition 2	15–27 months	Transition to adult method of communication	First words; first grinding tooth; walking
Verbal socialization (juvenile)	27 months–7 or 8 years	Development of verbal communication and understanding; perfection of motor skills	Beginning to talk in sentences

The dog is unique among mammals whose development is well-known in that all of its transition processes from neonatal to adult existence are concentrated in one short period. By contrast, human transitions are more extended and overlap more with other basic developmental processes and periods. The most striking difference, however, is that the human period of primary socialization comes before the transition to the adult form of locomotion. This means that human primary social relationships are inevitably formed with adult or semi-adult caretakers, usually the mother or a mother substitute. On the basis of the known facts of human development we would predict that primary social attachments should be easily formed at any time between approximately six weeks and six months of life and that these should be formed with increasing difficulty thereafter. Furthermore, any complete change of social relationships, such as that resulting from adoption, must involve the breaking off of emotional attachments, with consequently greater emotional disturbances as the child becomes older. These findings have great significance for the process of adoption. Indeed, most data on the effects of adopting children at different ages show that later emotional disturbances and maladjustments are much more common in children adopted in the second six months than in the first six months. This fact also poses the theoretical and practical problem of devising better ways of minimizing the risk of emotional disturbance in later periods.

The complexity of development of learning capacities. Such evidence as we now possess indicates that learning capacities in the neonatal period are quite limited and that consequently the results of early learning in this period are likely to have only limited effects upon later behavior. On the other hand, the risk of physical damage is greater than in later life because physiological developmental processes are still proceeding rapidly. On the basis of present information, we can say that the neonatal period is one in which the risks of physiological damage to the nervous system are much greater than those for psychological damage.

This situation changes rapidly as the child grows older. By two or two and a half months of age, the human infant can learn certain things quite rapidly, especially in the form of making simple associations and forming habits. Information received through verbal communication is not possible in any great quantity before approximately two years of age and is limited even at that time. Consequently there is a period of two years in which the infant can learn things on a non-verbal basis before he begins to learn through words. Whether this early learning is actually as lasting and permanent as later learning has never been established, but presumably it is. However, as anyone knows, what is learned in infancy is ordinarily not accessible through verbal recall. The earliest conscious memories of most people do not go back much earlier than three years.

This fact makes possible a situation not found in other species, in that what is learned on a verbal basis may conflict with what is learned on a non-verbal basis. There is every reason to suppose that while verbal learning is ordinarily dominant in the control of human behavior, the process of non-verbal learning continues throughout life. The result is that conflict is always possible between verbally learned material and that which is learned on another basis, whether in early infancy or in later life. The normal course of human development thus supports Freud's theories of the conscious and unconscious mind, to use the now rather old-fashioned language current in his day.

Of course it is also possible that preverbal learning is impermanent and has little or no effect on later behavior, or that because it is not ordinarily associated with what is learned on a verbal basis later, it is stored in such a way as to be inaccessible. Here again, we need more facts on the nature of human development.

Armed with this outline of the general course of human development and knowing something of the different courses of development through which other animals pass, we can now begin to analyze in a meaningful way some of the modifying factors which arise in early experience.

3 THE PRENATAL DEVELOPMENT OF BEHAVIOR

When does behavior begin? The early biologists thought that human beings were preformed in the egg and that the embryo was a miniature baby which only had to swell up to the usual size in order to be born. However, the invention of the microscope soon showed them that human life, like all other life, begins as a single cell, the fertilized egg. Although chemical activity and movement occur inside it the egg shows no behavior, if behavior is defined in the strict sense of activity of the whole organism. Behavior therefore has to be developed, and developed under the influence of all sorts of internal and external factors.

Nevertheless, the egg develops in a very predictable fashion. Obviously, the human egg, if it develops at all, always develops into a human being rather than into a chicken or a rabbit or a fox. This predictable element in development is often attributed to heredity alone, but as we shall see, heredity is only one of many organized systems which control the development of behavior, and variations in any one of these will modify it in various ways. The end result is that, while all human eggs normally develop into recognizable human beings, no two of these beings are ever exactly alike—not even identical twins.

HEREDITY AND BEHAVIOR

The first organized system to affect development is that of heredity. By this we mean the collection of fifty thousand or more gene pairs which are carried on the chromosomes of each individual. Each of these gene pairs can vary through the process of mutation, and the total genetic system of the human species consists of all of the genes carried by the billions of individuals now living. This is often called the "gene pool," because each individual withdraws a particular set of genes at birth and returns some of them to the common pool in the keeping of his own offspring.

The chemical nature of the genes. It is now known that genes are composed of highly complex proteins known as nucleic acids and that they produce their effects through chemical action, either directly or by producing enzymes which affect other chemical reactions. This means that heredity can directly affect only chemical reactions, and therefore that all genetic effects on behavior must be indirect. Some genes affect growth and may produce the difference between a tall, long-legged individual who thus has some aptitude for jumping and a short-legged person who has less of this aptitude. Other genes affect the chemistry of pigment formation and so may determine the difference between a blond and a brunette, and thus influence his or her attractiveness to certain members of the opposite sex. But gene action can take place in other ways than through growth or structure. It may also affect any chemical reactions going on in the body at any time during life, including those processes directly concerned with nerve action. Therefore, these genetic differences can appear very early in development or at any time in later life. A well-known example of early effects is the disease of phenylpyruvic oligophrenia, marked by the accumulation of an unmetabolized chemical, phenylalanine, beginning at birth. This substance in turn inhibits intellectual development unless the condition is controlled. At the other end of life, the symptoms of Huntington's chorea, a degenerative disease of the nervous system produced by the presence of a dominant gene, may not appear until sometime in the forties, the individual having led a normal life up to that point.

The principle of variation. The heredity of any species of animals is an organized system which has the general function of producing similar individuals. At the same time, the system of transmission which involves the chromosomes carrying the genes is also one which has an opposing function, that of producing dissimilar individuals. Each parent transmits to a particular child only half of his chromosomes, and these are chosen purely at random. Since the genes carried on the chromosomes vary through the process of mutation, the chromosomes of each child are never exactly alike. Through the process of "crossing over," or exchange of genes between chromosome pairs, identical chromosomes are never available for successive offspring. Each time a sperm or an egg cell is formed, the chromosomes pair together, break in various places, and reconnect with the opposite member of the pair. The location of a break is a matter of chance. Consequently it is almost impossible for two genetically identical individuals to be produced except in the rare case of identical twins which come from the same egg. Even in this case, the two twin embryos grow up in different parts of the uterus and therefore live in different environments from the very first moments of life.

Yet this genetic variation can exist only within certain limits. If a mutation or an unusual combination of genes produces too great a disturbance in the total genetic system, the individual may not be able to develop properly and may die at some stage in development.

Genic disturbances of development. When a gene is chemically altered, the result is called a mutation. The nature of such changes has been extensively studied in fruit flies and also in bacteria. Mutation rates vary considerably, as some genes are much more stable than others; but on the average a particular gene will mutate in one out of every million individuals in each generation under normal conditions. This rate can be greatly speeded up by X rays. In fact, radiation either from X rays used as clinical tools or from radioactive materials forms a major modern hazard to the genes.

Newer discoveries of the chemical nature of the genes have made it possible to produce mutational changes in bacteria deliberately. Unlike mutations produced by X rays, these are specific in nature, and geneticists now anticipate the future possibility of producing controlled mutations in the higher animals and in man. However, a gene is one part of an extremely complex system composed of 50,000 or more similar parts, all adjusted to and interacting with each other. A change in any one gene is much more likely to disturb the normal functioning of the system than to improve it. To use a mechanical analogy, reaching into an automobile engine and turning a screw at random is much more likely to disturb the running of the engine than to improve it. Similarly, the effect of the vast majority of chance mutations is deleterious. Many of them result in the early death of the embryo, and others produce various anatomical and physical malfunctions which may have an effect upon behavior.

Chromosomal disturbances of development. Changes in the normal form and numbers of chromosomes may occur as the result of faulty cell division. Ordinarily the pairs of chromosomes divide and separate equally, and each daughter cell gets the normal number. Occasionally, however, a chromosome pair may stick together, with the result that one cell lacks a chromosome and the other has one too many. The condition of Mongolian idiocy is produced by such a chromosomal accident; here the individual has three of one particular chromosome instead of the usual pair. Very frequently such chromosomal abnormalities result in early death of the embryo, but in this case the individual is viable enough to be born and live for at least a few years, although he is highly susceptible to certain kinds of disease.

Similar abnormalities in the distribution of other chromosomes also have anatomical and behavioral consequences, and those concerning the sex chromosomes have particularly interesting effects on behavior. Ordinarily, the female human being has two X chromosomes and the male has an XY. When two chromosomes do not separate, the result may be more than the usual number of either X or Y chromosomes. In the human species, the result can be to suppress or distort the development of the various sex organs and thus affect both bodily appearance and fertility.

The assortment and transmission of either chromosomal or genic abnormalities are almost completely matters of chance, and their occurrence can consequently be predicted only in terms of probabilities. Estimates indicate that each human being carries, on the average, two recessive lethal genes. Whether or not these affect the next generation depends upon whether or not the individual selects a mate who carries the same lethal genes. The frequencies of genes which are not lethal but have deleterious effects on behavior are known in some cases. For example, albinism, which totally removes pigment from the skin, hair, and eyes, occurs in about one out of 20,000 individuals and affects behavior in that the eyesight of an albino individual is very weak and in that he cannot expose himself to sunlight without suffering burns.

As in the case of albinism, most genes that produce unfavorable effects tend to be rare. Perhaps the commonest gene of this sort is that producing color blindness, which affects one out of twelve males and one out of 100 females. As a rule, however, the vast majority of babies are born with a reasonably good combination of genes and no crippling defects. Heredity thus operates very much like a lottery, but one in which the results are biased in favor of the gambler rather than against him. There is always an element of risk, but an individual has a good chance to draw a favorable combination of genes from the gene pool.

THE EGG AS AN ENVIRONMENT

The genes themselves operate within the environment of a cell, and the first contact of the newly organized genetic system formed by fertilization is with the cytoplasm of the egg. This itself is a system of organic chemicals organized under the influence of the mother's genes and developed in the environment provided by her ovary. Experiments with the eggs of lower animals show that even if the nucleus is removed, a properly stimulated egg will go through the first few cell divisions without the presence of the genes. The cytoplasmic system comes under genic control only gradually, and its condition modifies the action of heredity.

After the egg is formed in the ovary, half of the chromosomes and the genes carried with them are discarded, with the result that when the set of chromosomes from the father is brought into the egg with the sperm, the new individual has the same number as the parents. This means that in every case the genes of the new individual begin operations in an environment (the egg) which was produced under the influence of a different set of genes. Ordinarily this produces no difficulty, but if the genes are sufficiently different, development may be disturbed. This effect is shown by experiments in which the nuclei from salamander eggs are removed and those from a different species are substituted. In some cases development proceeds fairly well, but in others it soon comes to a halt, indicating that there must be a different chemical organization of eggs developed under different heredities. This principle would also apply, but with less drastic effects, to eggs normally produced and fertilized in the same species.

In addition to these gene-induced differences in the composition of the cytoplasm, the eggs can be modified by environmental factors or simply by the passage of time. There have been few attempts to actually alter the chemical constitution of eggs, but it is well established that if an egg is not fertilized soon after being shed from the ovary, the chance of normal development decreases. Presumably the egg deteriorates with age; in other words, a stale egg has a lessened chance of normal development.

Ordinarily eggs are developed under highly protected conditions within the body and so provide a highly uniform environment for the action of the genes. Each mother should therefore produce eggs closely similar to each other, except for rare environmental accidents and, of course, the fact that each one carries a different set of genes.

PRENATAL ENVIRONMENT

Homeostasis. As the French physiologist Claude Bernard pointed out long ago, a great many physiological processes are concerned with maintaining a constant internal environment. The American physiologist Walter Cannon called the phenomenon *homeostasis* and established it as one of the broad general principles of physiology.

As a result of homeostatic activity, human body temperature is ordinarily regulated within a fraction of a degree and with a dependability not exceeded by the finest of mechanical thermostats (there are few thermostats that will continue to operate for 70 or 80 years). Consequently the human embryo develops at a uniform temperature within its mother's body. In the early stages its cells and tissues are extremely delicate, and it is protected from the effects of touch and contact by being bathed in fluids. As it grows older the embryo develops within the amnion, a fluid-filled sac. Thus it is actually

Table 3.1 Major Periods of Prenatal Human Development

Period	Approximate Age after Conception	Major Processes
Cleavage	0	Cell division; growth begins
Implantation	9–10 days	Improved nutrition, acceleration of growth
Germ-layer formation	2 weeks	Organization of growth processes
Embryonic organ formation	3 weeks	Nerve tube, somites, limb buds, etc., formed by differential growth
Adult organ formation	5 weeks	Embryonic organs transformed by tissue formation into functional organs
Fetal	8 weeks–9 months	First motor behavior; organization through nervous stimulation begins

living under water, receiving equal support in all directions, and is little affected by gravity. No light reaches the embryo, and sound can reach it only through vibrations in the surrounding fluid.

The chemical environment is likewise highly regulated. The mother's liver has the function of regulating the food substances in the blood so that there is no wave of new chemical substances after each meal. This organ also has the ability to denature many poisonous substances which may enter the blood stream. Oxygen and carbon dioxide are kept at relatively constant levels by alterations in rates of the mother's breathing and blood circulation.

Under ordinary conditions, a cyclical fluctuation occurs in the female hormones connected with the menstrual cycle. During pregnancy, a more stable condition is maintained with the result that the embryo is given a uniform environment in this respect throughout prenatal development.

In spite of all these mechanisms for maintaining stability, homeostasis may sometimes be upset, as it is in the case of disease which produces a fever. In a time of famine, a mother who is actually starving may be unable to maintain a sufficient supply of food substances within her blood stream to maintain the growing embryo. Under other conditions, the liver may be unable to manage certain drugs and poisons, especially if the mother takes these in large quantities. At very high altitudes, the mother may be unable to supply the embryo with enough oxygen. Finally, hormonal balance may be upset by violent emotional experiences which affect the hormones produced by the adrenal glands.

The possible effects of upsetting homeostasis and thus altering the prenatal environment can only be ascertained by experiment, and studies are now being made with various lower animals. While the results cannot be transferred directly to human development, certain general principles have been established regarding the times at which variations in the prenatal environment produce important effects.

The principle of critical periods. Table 3.1 shows the major periods of early human development and their approximate timing. In general, the most drastic effects upon development are produced before the fetal period, which begins at approximately three months. Furthermore, in the periods preceding this, the earlier a disturbance is produced, the more general and the more drastic are its effects. For example, a disturbance during the period of cleavage may result in the separation of the egg and the production of identical twins or, less fortunately, in the production of Siamese twins or even a double monster. Disturbances in the period of germ-layer formation may result in part of the brain failing to develop.

The time of implantation is a critical period, for if the egg does not become attached to the uterus it is discharged and lost. Likewise, the period of forming the attachment of the placenta is critical, because without this form of nutrition normal development cannot proceed.

Most injuries during these early periods either result in the death of the embryo or in such a drastic alteration of form that the individual cannot survive beyond birth. However, during the period of embryonic organ formation damage may be much more specific and not as lethal. A dramatic example of a non-lethal effect resulted from the administration of thalidomide to pregnant women. This drug has a specific effect on the development of the limb buds, with the result that otherwise normal infants were born without arms or legs.

Minor disturbances affecting the embryonic organs result in less drastic effects. The embryonic eye is one of the most susceptible of these organs, because even a minor change in the shape of the lens or eyeball will drastically upset its future function. A large number of eye defects are probably caused by accidental embryonic damage.

The general principle of critical periods is based on the fact that any organ or part of the body which is undergoing rapid organization—and hence rapid growth—is unusually susceptible to damage. In the early periods of development when whole areas of the body are being organized, the effects of such damage are widespread and general. Later on, when specific organs or parts are being organized, the results are less drastic. We can therefore say that for each sort of effect there is a critical period at some time in development.

This same principle of critical periods limits the effects both of the chemical action of the genes and of chemical disturbances produced by various environmental accidents. There is no way of determining by inspection whether a particular kind of variation in development is produced by heredity or environmental factors. The only way to be sure is to experimentally demonstrate that the altered development is preceeded by a specific change, or to show that the same condition is also present in the individual's relatives in a pattern consistent with Mendelian inheritance.

The effects of experience during the fetal period. The fetal period is usually defined as starting when movement of the body begins, and extending up to birth. It is therefore the time during which behavior actually begins. The fetus is far less susceptible than the early embryo to environmental changes, and the period is characterized primarily by growth in size rather than by rapid changes in organization.

One would expect, therefore, that environmental factors in this period would have their chief effect on growth. For example, experiments with other animals show that the size of the mother has considerable effect upon the size of the baby, irrespective of genetics.

Horses belonging to the very large breed of draft animals known as Shires have been crossed experimentally with Shetland ponies. The colt receives the same heredity no matter which way the cross is made, but the newborn colt born to a Shetland pony mother is smaller than one born to a Shire mother. The difference is apparently caused by the fact that a larger placenta develops in the Shire. Consequently, more food is received by the growing embryo. The same principle has been established even more clearly by taking fertilized eggs from a small breed of sheep and transplanting them into a mother from a large breed. The newborn lambs are much larger than they would have been had they developed within the body of a small mother (Hammond, 1961).

The only human evidence we have of such uterine environmental effects is that afforded by twins, which are smaller on the average than babies from a single birth and hence have a somewhat smaller chance of survival. Here again, there is probably only a limited amount of room within the uterus for the development of a placenta or placentas.

Because the fetus grows so remarkably within the space of six months—from an embryo an inch or two in length to a newborn baby weighing six pounds or more and measuring approximately ten times as long—we should not suppose that the development of the various organs is complete. Of particular importance is the development of the endocrine system, which exercises chemical control over physiology and behavior.

The fetal period is also the time during which many of the basic biological characteristics of sex are determined. It has long been known that if the male hormone is accidentally given to a female fetus, it will produce masculinization. Such masculinization frequently appears in the case of twins in cattle. If a male and female are born together and there has been some intermixture of blood in the two placentas, the female turns out to be sterile and is called a freemartin.

Why does a human mother not show the effects of the male hormone when she is carrying a baby boy? Male hormones are sometimes given to women for medical reasons, and one of the undesirable side effects is the growth of facial hair in a masculine pattern. However, pregnant women are completely resistant to the virilization effects of the hormone. During pregnancy a mother produces an excessive amount of the female hormone, estrogen, and this apparently protects her against the action of the male hormones of her unborn boy.

As we have seen above, unborn female infants (at least in some species) are not protected against the effects of male hormones. Young and his co-workers (1964) have shown that injecting male hormones into a pregnant monkey bearing a genetically female fetus will produce a masculinized infant that not only shows sex organs which appear to be those of a male but also exhibits more masculine behavior than normal females. The hormone therefore modifies the development of the nervous system during the fetal stage, as well as modifying the external appearance of the individual.

Ordinarily, the developing fetus is protected against the kind of drastic interference with development which can be produced experimentally, but various accidents happen often enough so that pseudo-hermaphrodites do occasionally occur among newborn human babies. Is such a baby doomed to abnormal behavior? As we shall see in a later chapter, human behavior is highly adaptable, and up to a certain age the human infant can readily adapt himself to either sex role, even though lacking the complete biological basis for it.

Another part of the endocrine system that develops rapidly during the fetal period is that which regulates physical reactions to the stress of pain, injury, and emotional excitement. This regulation is accomplished chiefly through the hormone cortisone, produced by the cortex of the adrenal gland. Thompson and his colleagues (1962) have trained female rats to become fearful and nervous by giving them electric shocks in a particular box. After they have become pregnant, they are placed again in the box and repeatedly given the same treatment but without electric shock. The effect is to make them afraid without actually hurting them while they are carrying their unborn young. The offspring of these rats are more nervous and fearful than those from control mothers, even if they are raised by foster mothers which have never had the frightening experience. These results correlate with the observation made on wild rats brought into the laboratory that there is a considerable reduction in "wildness" after two or three generations even when no genetic selection is made for tamer animals.

Whether or not this effect could be duplicated with experiments on human mothers is still unknown, and in fact, verification would be almost impossible because of the tremendous individual variation among human beings, even if mothers would consent to being frightened. The most that can be said at present is that such a possibility does exist, and it is known that the unborn babies of mothers undergoing emotional disturbances are more active than those of calmer mothers. Many circumstances, however, determine whether being an anxious and nervous individual is an asset or a liability. In times of real danger, a nervous individual might be more likely to survive than a stolid one.

Moreover, this maternal effect on emotionality is not the same phenomenon as that described in the old wives' tales of "prenatal impressions," which were based on notions of sympathetic magic. According to these tales, a mother frightened by a horse might have a baby with a birthmark which looked like a horse, and so forth. No known mechanism exists by which such an effect could be produced. Prenatal experience may affect later behavior in more severely damaging ways than the above. Determining the time when a prenatal disturbance of the maternal environment took place is not always easy, but in any woman whose medical history is known, it is at least possible to know that complications of pregnancy such as toxemia have actually occurred. Pasamanick and Knobloch (1961) studied the relationship between prenatal experience and certain behavorial disorders and found that cerebral palsy, epilepsy, mental deficiency, and behavior disorders were correlated both with complications of pregnancy and with prematurity. They believe that these effects were probably the result of oxygen deficiency produced by such conditions as toxemia and maternal bleeding.

They further found that these damaging prenatal experiences and their associated behavorial deficiencies were more commonly found in mothers coming from lower socio-economic levels than in mothers from more prosperous homes. Since a disproportionate number of Negroes were found in lower economic levels, the figures for defective children were proportionately higher among Negroes. In addition, the experimenters found that an unusual number of neonatal deaths resulted from pregnancies initiated in the spring, that is, in pregnancies whose first three months occured during hot weather. Again, the effects were much more severe for mothers in the lowest economic levels. While no 1:1 correlation exists between poverty and prenatal damage, it is difficult to avoid the conclusion that the condition of poverty in our society produces a circular effect. Children born of poor parents are more likely to have certain defects, and because of these will be less likely to be able to provide their own children with a favorable prenatal environment.

Providing the unborn infant with an adequate supply of oxygen appears to be particularly important in the last stages of pregnancy when the fetus is becoming quite large. Babies born at high altitudes —especially those of over 10,000 feet—show a much higher rate of prematurity and hence run a much greater risk of neonatal death (Grahn and Kratchman, 1963). This condition applies to a few areas in the Rocky Mountain states and is, of course, much more severe in some of the South American equatorial highlands, where many people live and work at altitudes of 14,000 feet or more. Historical records show that in the early days of the Spanish conquest there were no living children born to Spanish families at the high-altitude city of Potosi (13,120 feet) in a period of over fifty years (Monge, 1948). When one child finally did survive, the event was officially listed as a miracle. Presumably by a process of selection, the native Indian children were and still are better able to survive at these high altitudes, but even they as adults show the physical effects of stress produced by lack of oxygen and exposure to ultra-violet rays.

In addition to the disturbances of the prenatal environment produced by unfavorable external conditions, the mother in any environment herself changes with age and so affects prenatal development. Figures on neonatal mortality show high death rates both in babies carried by young girls and by older women, indicating that the most favorable period for child bearing is the early twenties, with a moderately favorable period on either side extending from 15 to 35 (see Table 3.2).

Table 3.2 Fetal Death Ratios by Age of Mother in 34 States in the U. S. (Gestation 20 weeks or longer)*

Age of Mother (Years)	Ratio: 1000 Live Births
Under 15	26.6
15–19	14.7
20–24	11.7
25–29	13.7
30–34	19.0
35–39	26.9
40 and over	38.7
Total, all ages	15.5

* Most states do not require registration of deaths taking place before 20 weeks, so that the great majority of miscarriages are not included in these figures. Note that the most favorable age of the mother for fetal survival is 20–24 years. Source: Vital Statistics of the United States, 1964, U.S. Public Health Service.

Similar results are obtained with other mammals. Very young mothers are less efficient, both physiologically and behaviorally, than those who are fully mature, while very old mothers have weaker offspring and are less able to suckle them. This does not mean that an individual is inevitably doomed because he is born to a very young or a relatively old mother; in human populations many normally hardy and healthy children are born under these circumstances. The probabilities of good health, however, are somewhat poorer for them than for children born to mothers in the mid-range. Parents who have a choice are wise to have their children during the most favorable age period.

In addition to these studies of the indirect effects of fetal experience upon later behavior, many studies have been made of fetal behavior itself. As any mother knows, her unborn baby becomes active enough to be felt at about four months of age and becomes increasingly so as it grows older. Early fetuses obtained as a result of operations or miscarriages show reactions to tactile stimulation as long as they survive. Such results indicate that much of the reflex behavior of a neonate appears long before birth.

Perhaps the most interesting studies are those of behavior of babies being carried by normal mothers who cooperated with the Fels Institute for the Study of Human Development (Sontag, 1944). Observers could readily detect and measure kicking, squirming, and hiccoughs through the abdominal wall of the mother, and found that babies are active about 15 per cent of the time at four months of pregnancy, increasing to 35 per cent by eight months. If a sudden vibration is applied to the mother's abdomen, the result is the startle or Moro reflex, accompanied by an increase in heart rate. The fetus will also respond to loud sounds received by the mother's abdomen through the air. The fetus is of course surrounded by water, which is an excellent transmitter of sound. Moreover, the mother is continually stimulating it by producing changes in internal pressures through breathing and other bodily movements.

Attempts have been made to condition the prenatal startle reflex, but the difficulty with all these experiments is that it is almost impossible to stimulate the fetus with anything that is not perceived by the mother. Since the fetal infants seem to condition more readily than neonates, it is quite probable that the mother is the one who is being conditioned rather than her offspring. In any case, the amount of information that a fetal infant could learn and organize within the highly protected and stable environment of a normal mother's body would be extremely limited, even if it possessed good learning capacities. Attempts to put adult individuals into similar situations in tanks of warm water and without sensory stimulation tend to produce disassociation and disorganization of behavior.

It is therefore possible to conclude that the effects of changes in the prenatal environment are largely physiological rather than psychological in nature. From the biological viewpoint, fetal behavior has chiefly a physiological adaptive function. Movements promote circulation, prevent the formation of adhesions to the surrounding membranes, and help develop and strengthen bones and muscles.

GENERAL EFFECTS OF PRENATAL EXPERIENCE

Prenatal development proceeds under the general control of three organized systems: the heredity of the individual, the egg and the composition of its contents, and the prenatal environment produced by the mother. Disturbances in any one of these systems can produce variations whenever they occur in the course of development, and hereditary and environmental factors can operate to produce such disturbances at any time in prenatal existence. The effect of a disturbance depends largely upon the stage of development. The most drastic effects are produced when particular processes are proceeding most rapidly. Thus numerous critical periods occur in development, that for one process being different from that in another, or perhaps overlapping with it. The same process may take place at different times in different organs, so that the timing of critical periods may be different for different organs. In general, the earlier the disturbance is produced, the more drastic the effects.

In this chapter we have given many examples of the deleterious effects of prenatal experience, chiefly because these are the ones which are easiest to produce and measure experimentally. However, there must be many minor effects which are less harmful and even beneficial.

The preponderance of harmful effects may also be related to the fact that it is easier to upset a highly organized system than to change it to produce a superior kind of organization. Moreover, we cannot deny the importance of such upsets. At least 20 per cent of all human pregnancies never come to term, and the figures for animal experiments, where the data are more accurate, run as high as 40 per cent. In human cases many terminated pregnancies undoubtedly occur without being reported, and if the egg dies early enough, the mother may never even notice it.

Such prenatal deaths should not be considered as tragedies, as the vast majority of them concern highly defective individuals produced by variations in either heredity or environment. In most cases it is a much greater tragedy if such a highly defective individual survives beyond birth.

Obviously, most variations in the prenatal environment are completely outside conscious control. The most that a mother can do is to make sure that she is leading a healthful existence and to give herself good physiological care and relatively placid surroundings. Most environmental accidents to which she herself is subjected will be taken care of by the normal homeostatic processes of her body. She should, however, guard against prolonged exposures to strong chemicals or drugs, which may enter her body either through food or through the air she breathes. She can also consult a clinic on medical genetics if she suspects that heredity diseases which she might transmit to her child are present in her family.

4 CRITICAL PERIODS OF SOCIAL DEVELOPMENT

Among animals living under natural conditions, the social environment is often the most stable feature of the surroundings. A lamb living in a flock of mountain sheep experiences changing weather conditions from day to day, and even from hour to hour as rain ceases and the sun comes out. Predators may be present one day and gone the next, and even the food supply varies enormously with the seasons. However, other members of the flock are always present. Individuals die and are replaced by younger ones, but reproduction always takes place in the same way year after year, and behavior develops in a very consistent fashion in succeeding generations.

Because of its stability, the important effects of the early social environment do not become apparent until experimenters interfere with it by drastic methods. For example, the behavior of domestic sheep develops in ways very similar to those of mountain sheep, generation after generation; but the simple act of taking a young lamb from its mother at birth and rearing it on a bottle away from the flock produces a radically different animal, one that stays apart from the flock and attempts to follow people everywhere like Mary's little lamb in the nursery rhyme.

Two general methods are used in this kind of experiment. One is to take a young mammal or bird from its parents at birth or hatching and rear it by hand away from its own kind. The second method is to take young animals and rear them in isolation, providing the equivalent of parental care by mechanical means. By these methods the important phenomenon of primary socialization, or imprinting, was discovered.

PRIMARY SOCIALIZATION (IMPRINTING)

One of the major functions of most highly developed animal societies is the care and protection of the young. In order for this to work efficiently the young animal must become attached to the members of its own species. It will not suffice for the newborn animal to have a generalized positive reaction to all members of its own species, for efficient care depends on its staying with particular individuals who are ready and equipped to give that care. Therefore, it must become attached to particular individuals and be able to discriminate between these and others. We call this process primary socialization, implying that this is the first way in which the behavior of the young animal becomes modified in relation to the rest of society, and we can define it as the formation of the first social relationships, and particularly the formation of emotional attachments. All the highly social animals which have been so far studied have a short period early in life when this process takes place.

Imprinting in birds. Birds are characteristically flying animals, but all are flightless as they emerge from the egg. Characteristically, most of them develop very rapidly so that they can reach the relative safety of the air as soon as possible. Some of the small perching birds are able to fly twelve or fourteen days after hatching, and even large birds like ducks and geese are very nearly full grown in about six weeks. The Japanese quail, a domestic bird noted for rapid development, may produce eggs as soon as eight weeks after its own egg was originally laid.

Some birds, like chickens and ducks, are born in a precocious state and are able to walk as soon as they are hatched. If eggs of these species are hatched in an incubator and the newly emerging young are shown only a model of a parent bird, they will soon begin to follow it. The model need not have any great resemblance to a bird, as young chicks will readily become attached to square boxes or round balloons. They will also become attached to almost any other living thing, from white rats to human beings. Using the right technique, it is easy to produce the comical effect of a chick following a person as if he were its mother. The peak of the imprinting effect occurs about seventeen hours after hatching and declines rapidly thereafter. By three or four days of age, young chicks become quite fearful of strange objects, and getting them to form an attachment becomes increasingly difficult (Hess, 1962).

Other birds are born in a very immature state. Most people are familiar with the blind and naked nestlings of the perching birds. These birds also form emotional attachments, but at a much later date and in a much more gradual way, with the result that hand rearing has little effect until a week or so after hatching. In doves and pigeons, whose newly hatched young are also helpless, the degree of attachment to a human being varies inversely with the age at which the young squab is removed from its parents' nest. Klinghammer (1967) found that mourning doves taken before 8 days never developed fears of human handlers, but those taken a day or two later showed fears as adults.

When begun at the proper time, hand-rearing has drastic effects on a bird's later behavior. A hand-reared male turkey, for example, may be able to mate with his own kind as an adult, but if he has a choice between another turkey and a human being, he will go to the human being—and perseveringly repeat the behavior patterns of courtship in spite of the fact that these do not produce any response. The result of primary socialization, or imprinting, has been to transfer the development of social relationships from one species to another. Because experience in the early period of primary socialization not only determines the nature of primary relationships but also indirectly determines the later ones, the period of primary socialization is a critical period for later development.

Primary socialization in mammals. Like birds, some mammals are precocious and others are born in various stages of immaturity. The large herd animals are all precocious, and the effects of hand rearing such animals are well known. Bottle-raised fawns become extremely tame and attached to people and lose so many of their "instinctive" fears that they are seldom able to survive if turned loose in the wilds afterwards.

Of all the herd animals we know most about domestic sheep and goats. If a young lamb is taken from its mother at birth and reared on a bottle, it becomes a most unsheeplike sheep, following people everywhere, unafraid of dogs, and independent of its own kind. It is unresponsive to other sheep even if raised in the same field with the flock, but the behavior which prevents its becoming attached to other sheep is that of the adult females rather than its own. The young lamb will approach the females but they always butt it away and reject it as they would any strange lamb. The young orphan lamb soon learns to stay away from them and develops its relationships only with people.

The length of the critical period for primary socialization in the young lamb has never been determined, but it must begin soon after birth and last for at least a week. On the other hand, the critical period for a mother forming an attachment to her own lamb is a matter of hours. If a mother has her lamb taken away at birth, she will accept it if it is brought back again within two to four hours and will "own" it during a somewhat longer period if she is kept isolated from other sheep in the meantime (Hersher *et al.* 1963). This emphasizes the fact that the relationship between mother and offspring is a dual one and that the mother forms an attachment to her offspring as well as the reverse.

The situation in slowly developing animals like the dog is quite different. The young puppy is born in a very immature state with respect to its sense organs, being both blind and deaf. Even the sense of smell is poorly developed. This means that the newborn puppy is unable to discriminate between one individual and another, and the process of forming an emotional attachment does not begin until the puppy is about three weeks of age.

By this time the sense organs have matured, and for the next several weeks the young puppy is able to form new relationships rapidly with any strange dog or human being. Although the first reaction to a stranger of a young puppy between three and seven weeks of age is to crouch down or escape, this response is only momentary. Within a few seconds or minutes it will approach and investigate, nosing the stranger's clothes, and wagging its tail. In one experiment, Freedman, King, and Elliot (1961) raised puppies in a one-acre field that was surrounded by a high board fence so that the animals could not see people. They were fed through a hole in the fence, and their only human contact came when they were removed for a week's socialization in the laboratory at different ages. By fourteen weeks of age, those pups which had no human contact were acting like little wild animals, but those with previous contact showed different degrees of positive attraction. This experiment showed that the peak of the ability to rapidly form a new social relationship occurs between six and eight weeks of age, declining thereafter with the increasingly prolonged fear responses to strangers. It is perhaps no accident that the peak of this capacity occurs very close to the time when a mother normally weans her puppies completely from the breast. At this age neither dogs nor their wild ancestors, the wolves, are truly self-sufficient, and wolf cubs continue to be fed by their elders, including other members of the pack as well as parents. It is therefore highly adaptive for the puppy to be able to form new relationships readily at this time. Whether similar timing occurs in other species is a matter for investigation.

Duration and nature of the critical period. As we have seen from these various examples, the critical period for primary socialization can be as short as a few hours in a rapidly developing animal like the chicken, or it can extend over a period of several weeks in a slowly developing mammal like the dog. All of the animals in which this phenomenon has been studied are alike in that they can form social attachments quite rapidly during the critical period.

In the dog, lasting effects can be produced by daily contacts extending over a period of as little as a week. Puppies reared in isolation during the critical period will develop normal relationships with people if allowed as little as two twenty-minute periods of contact per week throughout the whole period of several weeks. All animals in which primary socialization has been studied are also alike

FIGURE 4.1   The effect of socialization on behavior. The 14-week-old beagle puppy at the top had one week of contact with people during the critical period, while the one at the bottom had no contact.

FIGURE 4.2 Response of a puppy to a stranger in the latter part of the period of socialization. If contact is not made, fear and avoidance reactions become increasingly strong, so that the formation of emotional attachments becomes more difficult as the animal gets older.

in that the critical period comes early in life, although not necessarily at the point immediately after hatching or birth.

What determines the length of the critical period and what brings it to a close? These questions raise the problem of the basic nature of the process involved. What exactly happens to an animal forming a strong social attachment? One clue comes from the fact that the attachments are made before the animal develops a strong fear response to strangers. A young chick or puppy does not quickly form a social relationship with a stranger after the critical period because its first response is to run away and stay away, thus effectively preventing any prolonged contact. Furthermore the fact of becoming attached to one individual and staying with it, as a chick stays with its mother, will keep it out of contact with other hens, not to mention other species of animals and particularly predators such as foxes.

Although this still does not answer the question of the nature of the positive mechanism of forming an attachment, all evidence indicates that emotional responses are involved. A young puppy will exhibit distress vocalization as soon as it it is removed from the familiar objects and individuals to which it becomes attached during the critical period. At six or eight weeks of age, a temporarily isolated puppy may average 140 vocalizations per minute and keep up this rate for hours. This obvious emotional distress is relieved by the presence of another individual or by familiar surroundings. Thus the puppy experiences an uncomfortable emotion which is relieved by staying with its own kind. The emotional reaction itself appears to be a very simple primary response that has the effect of maintaining an attachment between the animal and another member of its own species. Furthermore, the effect of artificially producing other unpleasant emotions, such as fear responses to noise or electric shock, is to intensify the reaction of staying with its own kind and to speed up the general process of attachment. The young animal must learn very quickly that being separated from familiar individuals is unpleasant and that being with them relieves this unpleasantness. In terms of learning theory, staying with familiar animals and persons is reinforced by the punishing effect of separation and the relief afforded by reunion (Scott, 1967).

General theory of critical periods. The concept of a critical period may be examined on several levels of complexity. Most superficially, a critical period is based on time, and within this dimension a critical period can be defined as a time when a large effect can be produced by a smaller change in conditions than in any later or earlier period in life. From this viewpoint, critical periods have enormous practical importance for the modification of behavior through training and education. In the case of the critical period for primary socialization, a small amount of contact at an early period in life will determine which individuals will be the close social relatives of the animal in its infancy and often for the rest of its life. A similar period of contact in adult life may produce only momentary reactions to passing strangers.

Considered more deeply, critical periods must depend on internal processes. There must be changes taking place within the animal which are correlated with time and hence account for the existence of critical periods. Time itself is a term of description and measurement rather than an explanatory concept. A fundamental question is: what changes go on within the individual which make a critical period in life different from any other? The most general answer is that a critical period is one in which rapid organization of some kind is taking place. While this is going on, it is easy to change the nature of the organization. However, organization in itself has a tendency to produce stability. *Therefore, any period in life when rapid organization is taking place is a critical period,* since the changes which are easily and often accidentally produced at that time become a fixed and relatively permanent feature of the stabilized organization (Scott, 1962). In the case of primary socialization, the young animal is organizing its first social relationships.

By extension we can reason that *any period in life when a major new relationship is being formed is a critical one for determining the nature of that relationship.* Such a period would occur in later life during courtship and mating and the resulting formation of the first sexual relationship, and we have already seen an example of a critical period in the formation of a relationship by the mother sheep for her offspring. Such a period should occur in any mammal when the young are born. The period of primary socialization is an unusually critical one in that it may indirectly affect the formation of these later relationships.

Periods and processes. From what has been said above it is obvious that the important thing about the process of primary socialization is not time, although this permits us to easily describe and predict events, but the actual process itself. Therefore, the things to look for in development are times at which organizational processes are proceeding at a maximum speed.

Primary socialization in human infants. As we saw in Chapter 2, there appears to be a definite neonatal period in human infants, extending from birth to about five or six weeks of age. During this period all behavior is organized around the problems of neonatal life, particularly that of neonatal nutrition, which is accomplished by suckling. Marked by the appearance of the smiling response to human faces, there is a period of rapid improvement in the capacity for visual perception. By six months of age, the decrease in rate of smiling to strangers indicates that the infant readily distinguishes between familiar and unfamiliar faces. The period from approximately five or six weeks to six or seven months of age is thus the period during which the process of primary socialization, or the formation of the first social relationships, takes place (Gray, 1958). One consequence of the timing of this period is that a young baby will usually form its first social relationships with its own parents. Since it usually has more contact with its mother than any other individual, the earliest, and presumably strongest, relationship will be formed with her, although under other conditions of child rearing it would be possible for a baby to form a strong relationship with any individual who took care of it. We have no data on how long a baby takes to form a lasting social relationship, but if results with other animals are any guide, it probably needs very little time. The baby's reactions are consistent with those of other animals in that its positive responses to a stranger during this period are easily and quickly evoked. The puppy during the critical period of socialization wags its tail at strangers, and the human infant smiles.

THE EFFECTS OF ISOLATION

Drastic experiments with social isolation of human infants are never performed for obvious reasons, and what evidence we have is confined to accidental cases in which children have been hidden from the outside world for criminal or emotional reasons. The most famous case is that of the "Nuremberg boy," Kaspar Hauser, who was discovered wandering in the streets as a young adult in the year 1828. He could at first speak little more than his own name but later reported that he had been kept in a dungeon without companions and that his only playthings were a toy dog and two hobbyhorses. He was therefore not only a social isolate but also the product of rearing in a barren environment. No information was available as to how early he was placed in isolation, and all that can be said is that he showed a considerable degree of recovery from its effects.

Results of animal experiments on isolation. Rearing a young bird or mammal in isolation from its own kind (and from any other species with which it might associate) produces bizarre and striking effects on behavior. The longer the isolation is continued the more drastic are the results. An isolated male Indian jungle fowl will as an adult attempt to go through the usual motions of courtship to a female but direct these toward his own body so that he spins and whirls in behavior never seen in ordinary roosters (Kruijt, 1964). A puppy isolated during the critical period will often show bizarre postures such as standing still in the corner of a room with one paw raised above its head and forced into the angle of the walls (Fuller and Clark, 1966a, 1966b).

From our understanding of the process of primary socialization, we would predict that the isolated animal would become attached to whatever was available in the environment during the critical period. The only living thing present is the animal itself. We would therefore predict that a chicken reared in isolation would become imprinted upon its own body and, indeed, the reaction of the isolated adult is consistent with this expectation. From experiments with attachments to inanimate models we would also predict that the isolated animal would become attached to anything present in the physical surroundings, such as food dishes or even the walls of the confining chamber. Thus isolated puppies after their release from confinement will sometimes play for hours with food and water dishes each in a solitary fashion. More than this, the effects of isolation upon the subsequent behavior of a puppy are bound up with the development of the capacity of fear. During isolation there is very little to frighten the young animal, but it nevertheless develops a capacity for a complete fear response. The result is that the release from isolation produces a strong fearful reaction which becomes associated with the entire outside world. The puppy standing in the corner is probably attempting to escape as far as possible from all the strange stimulation around it, or perhaps it is trying to draw some comfort from contact similar to the walls of its box.

Results of semi-isolation on human behavior. As indicated above, drastic isolation experiments are never done on children, but isolation occurs commonly enough in normal experience for us to know something of its effects. Short periods of isolation produce crying and a strongly unpleasant emotional reaction; in fact, temporary isolation was formerly often used as a method of punishment for young children, just as solitary confinement is still occasionally used as a drastic punishment for adult prisoners.

Children's lives differ a great deal with respect to the number and closeness of social contacts that are permitted during early development. Some children grow up in remote rural areas with a limited group of family acquaintances, and others are deliberately exposed to a large number outside the family, as in the case of those who are sent to nursery school. We would predict that the result of semi-isolation would be the development of shyness with strangers, and this seems to be the case with children brought up in isolated rural environments where they may never see anyone except members of their immediate families during their early years. However, there is undoubtedly wide variation in emotional responses among children, and some should have a much greater hereditary capacity for the development of shyness than others. Effects of rearing in such an environment should therefore vary among individuals.

A much more serious disturbance of behavior is the development of autism. An autistic child tends to play entirely by himself and to be unresponsive to others. The symptoms, at least, are very similar to those of young animals raised in isolation, but the circumstances are different. Such children usually live in what seem to be normal family surroundings. Some evidence indicates that their parents are not warmly emotional, but this explanation hardly seems adequate, especially in view of the tendency of animals to become attached to completely unresponsive objects. The autistic child behaves as if he had become socialized only to himself. We can hypothesize that there has been some derangement of the whole process of socialization, that the derangement is definitely connected with the development of emotional reactions, and that it may have a partially hereditary basis.

RESULTS OF BREAKING A SOCIAL RELATIONSHIP

Unlike rearing in isolation, the breaking off of a social relationship is something which frequently happens in human development as a result of death, illness, financial misfortunes, and other disruptions of family life. The practical problems of replacing such relationships through adoption, together with its frequently unfavorable results, have inspired a considerable amount of observational work. The psychiatrist John Bowlby (1951) became interested in the results of broken relationships when he studied the case histories of a group of juvenile thieves and discovered that a large number of them had been separated from their mothers for long periods during infancy. He and his associates then made first-hand studies of children as they were separated from their parents, particularly in cases of hospitalization, which can necessitate an abrupt, drastic and long-lasting separation from familiar surroundings. They found that children are indeed seriously upset by these experiences, and their results have prompted many children's hospitals to change their practices through encouraging frequent visits by parents and by decreasing the time of separation as much as possible.

Primary results of separation in infants. As we saw in Chapter 2, Schaffer (1958) found two kinds of reactions in babies returned to their homes after a period of separation in hospitals. Before seven months such babies show what he calls a "global syndrome", becoming depressed and staring anxiously at everything in the room, living and non-living. After seven months, the babies show an "overdependency syndrome". They cry a great deal and try to avoid being separated from anyone who is caring for them. The earlier reaction is related to change in the physical environment and indicates that the babies have become attached to their surroundings and are disturbed by leaving them. This reaction is undoubtedly related to the process of localization, or becoming attached to a particular place, which will be discussed again in Chapter 6. The changed reaction after seven months indicates that the baby is now reacting primarily to the separation from people, which is equivalent to the temporary breaking of a social relationship.

Permanent separation produces more drastic effects. Yarrow (1964) studied a group of seventy-five infants that were transferred to a foster mother sometime during their first year. A few showed distress when transferred as early as three months, but by six months 86 per cent showed serious emotional disturbances, and all infants over seven months showed reactions severe enough to be called emotional trauma.

Bowlby (1960) and his colleagues have also studied the degree of emotional disturbance produced by separation at various ages. During the second half of the first year, the emotional reaction to separation may appear after only a few hours. As a child grows older, he becomes more and more capable of managing separation for long periods, particularly after he has learned to talk and begins to have some concept of the time at which his parents may return.

Most parents are familiar with the emotional symptoms of separation when they leave their children for a few days to travel or take a vacation. The baby-sitter or caretaker of course finds that the children are emotionally disturbed and hard to handle, being given to frequent crying and periods of depression. An experienced baby-sitter soon learns to try to keep the children amused and stimulated and thus counteracts the emotion of depression in her charges. On their return, the parents find the children tearful, demanding, and sometimes antagonistic. They often conclude that this behavior is the result of the baby-sitter's "spoiling" them. Actually, the children have been emotionally hurt by their parents and react in various ways. Some of these seem to be simple attempts to punish the parents. If the separation has been unusually long, a child may react with real coldness, as if reluctant to enter into a close social relationship again and thus run the risk of future separations and the resulting emotional pain. Obviously, breaking a social relationship, even temporarily, is a serious matter for a child. Although separation can never be completely avoided, and perhaps should not be, parents should manage it as carefully as possible, especially in the case of younger children.

Adoption. From a theoretical viewpoint, any emotional damage which might result from adoption should be the effect not of forming a new relationship but of breaking off an old one. The more well established the original relationship, the more the child should be disturbed by breaking it, but this principle is limited by the fact that as a child becomes older he can understand the circumstances better and protect himself against their emotional consequences. We shall discuss here only the effects of breaking a relation in infancy.

The theoretically ideal time for an adoption is, of course, soon after birth and no later than the end of the neonatal period. At this age the baby should react to its adopted parents just as it would to its real ones, and their only concern should be to give it the good physical care that any baby should have. If adoption takes place during the period of socialization, extending from five or six weeks to approximately six or seven months, a new relationship should be formed with ease, but most easily toward the beginning of the period rather than the end. Some immediate emotional upset would be expected, in accordance with Schaffer's observations, but this should be as much the result of the change in locality as the break in a primary social relationship.

Once the primary social relationship has been strongly established and the fear reaction to strangers has begun to appear, a much more severe emotional upset should result. Indeed, such objective evidence as is available indicates that children who have been separated from familiar persons and surroundings and adopted in the second half of the first year are more likely to show later difficulties of personal adjustment than those adopted in the first. It is, however, difficult to tell how much of this maladjustment is due to permanent emotional damage suffered by the infant at the time, and how much is due to the pattern of parent-child relationships which is being organized for the first time immediately after adoption and whose effects continue long into the future. Any continuing social relationship is a two-way affair, and unless foster parents are aware of the problems of adoption and are able to make emotional readjustments of their own, the habits and attitudes that they set up during their own critical period of emotional adjustment and behavioral organization will almost certainly be different towards a fearful, emotionally disturbed infant than toward a normally clinging and welcoming one.

Various circumstances such as death or lack of foster parents available to take an orphan at the most suitable time may make adoption necessary at various periods later than the optimum. If such an unavoidable situation arises care should be taken to make the transition as smooth as possible. For example, the prospective parents can be introduced to their new child in his own familiar environment and their visits repeated over a period of several hours or even days in such a way that the child can overcome his fear of strange people without having to contend with the fear of strange surroundings at the same time. Second, the transition can be made in such a way that the child is taken into his new environment for a few hours only and then returned to his original home before being taken away for good. Returning the child more often might also be desirable in order to preserve some continuity between his former and future existences.

To summarize: All evidence from both human development and that of other social mammals indicates that even temporarily breaking contact with individuals and surroundings to which a primary attachment has taken place is a strongly disturbing emotional experience. This reaction has undoubtedly evolved as an adaptation to being lost or separated from the familiar. For a young and dependent social mammal, such a situation is often extremely dangerous. Unless the infant gives an immediate emotional reaction and starts signaling its whereabouts, its life may be lost within a few hours. Hence the distress vocalization of young puppies and the crying responses of human babies when left alone in strange places have strong survival value.

The results of permanent separation and the consequent complete break in a strongly developed social relationship are serious at any time in life, as anyone knows who has experienced the death of a close relative or the breakup of a marriage. For a young infant, the problem of permanent separation is usually settled by adoption, and here we can learn much from experiments with dogs, whose adoption (by the human species) is a normal occurrence. Much can be done to alleviate the painful emotions produced by separation, but the adopted puppy almost inevitably becomes more sensitive to separation and, consequently, more dependent on its human foster parents. These characteristics are desirable in a dog, as few people want a completely independent pet, but less so in a child, who should eventually develop into an independent and responsible adult. The answer seems to be to manage the child's separation in such a way as to decrease the painful emotional reactions as much as possible and to allow him an opportunity to integrate and organize the two portions of his existence.

FAMILY RELATIONSHIPS

Human babies may be brought up in widely different social environments, depending upon the composition of the particular family into which they are born. In the United States, we are likely to think of a family as consisting of a mother, father, and children, but other societies may have families organized on quite different bases, involving such customs as polygamy, the presence of several generations under one roof, or even multiple households. Even in our own society, the nuclear family of one male, one female, and their children may be broken up by death or divorce, and there are still families in which older relatives are permanent members of the household.

Besides these variables, the social environment of a child can differ according to his ordinal position in the family (that is, whether he is first, second, or third, and so on), the sex of his siblings and their relative ages, and the total family size. Finally, the age of his parents and their own early experience of family life may influence the kind of care and attention which they give him.

The members of a family do not act as individuals but in relation to each other, and in so doing they develop social relationships, which may be defined as regular and consistent behavior between individuals. A relationship is never completely stable but is always changing in a developmental, and hence somewhat predictable, fashion. The most important determinants of a simple relationship between two individuals are the sex and relative age of the two persons concerned. The most important difference in age is, of course, that between a child and a mature adult. In the examples given below, we are going to assume a simplified family structure in which both parents and no other adults are present. Therefore, the basic relationship in the family group is one developed between an adult male and an adult female. Adding a male child to the family adds two new relationships, that between an adult male and a young male and that between an adult female and a young male (Figure 4.3). If the child is a female, two different relationships are added, those between an adult male and a young female and between an adult female and a young female. Thus, while we have only two *combina-*

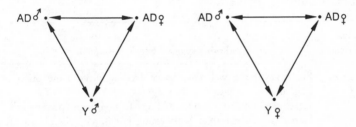

FIGURE 4.3 Combinations of social relationships in one-child families. There are four kinds of individuals (adult males and females, young males and females), resulting in five kinds of relationships in two combinations.

tions of relationships resulting from the addition of either a male or female child to the family, there are actually five different *kinds* of relationships developed in the two sorts of one-child families.

The one-child family. With the exception of a family in which the first birth is a multiple one, all families obviously go through a one-child stage. When it becomes extended over a long period, a one-child family can usually be explained by such special circumstances as the parents' infertility, advanced age at marriage, ill health, or dislike of children. Family behavior and organization may be greatly affected by whether the child is a boy or a girl, but in any case the obvious result is a triangular set of social relationships (Figure 4.3). Each member of the family is responding to two other individuals, which may make adjustment difficult. In such a situation, the child may easily learn to play off one parent against the other, and a father is almost inevitably jealous of his wife's transfer of affection and attention to the first baby. However, if the family can make satisfactory adjustments, its relationships are likely to be very close. In their study of child-rearing practices in modern American culture, Sears, Maccoby, and Levin (1957) found—as might be expected—that parents give considerably more individual attention to only children than to members of a larger family.

Table 4.1 Tendencies toward Differential Early Training Received by Children in Different Family Positions (In Families Studied by Sears, Maccoby, and Levin)

Position in Family	Training and Early Environment
Oldest child	Pregnancy more welcome; breast feeding given more often and lasts longer. Aggression toward younger siblings treated more permissively. Father more strict than with younger children; disciplined often by father when both parents present.
Middle child	Given bowel training later, least attention and play with mother; given more jobs.
Youngest child	Pregnancy least welcome, breast feeding given least often and relatively short; weaned with most severity. Given most praise for playing well with siblings. Deprivation of privileges used less often, disciplined more often by mother when father present.
Only child	Pregnancy highly welcome; breast feeding short and weaning severe. Mother gives much attention and opportunity for play. Mother more often the disciplinarian when both parents present.

These differences are not absolute and hence do not necessarily apply to individual cases. They represent average tendencies; for example, 72% of fathers were delighted by a first pregnancy, whether of a first child or an only child, while 58% were delighted when their wives became pregnant with a middle or a youngest child.

The most obvious consequence of being an only child is the lack of other siblings, so that he never has the opportunity to develop relationships within the family with persons near his own age. The only child is spared any experience with sibling rivalry, but he never learns to adapt to any other children in his home, and he never has close family models of behavior except his parents, who are much older than he. However, most of the unique consequences of being an only child appear in later experience, for during his first two years or so his lot should be very much like that of an oldest child in a more numerous family.

The two-child family. Such a family can be composed of two boys, two girls, or a girl and boy in either order, making four different sorts of groups and eight possible family positions. Thus a boy can be either younger or older, and have either a boy or a girl as a sibling, and the same four positions are duplicated for girls.

The relationships developed between these individuals are much more complex than in the one-child family. Four different kinds of relationships can be developed between the siblings, and each of the parents can develop four kinds of relationships with their children, depending on their sex and relative age. Finally there is the relation between the parents, making a total of thirteen different kinds of relationships, which are combined in four different combinations (Figure 4.4).

Whatever its composition, the two-child family has the advantage that its members can separate into pairs. If one child is receiving the attention of the mother, the other can go to the father. Or, if father and mother are responding to each other, the two children can play together. Any combination of this sort is much easier to adapt to than a triangular one.

The oldest child, in a family of any size, has various peculiar circumstances in his environment. In the first place, he is the one on whom the parents learn about child rearing. Being uncertain themselves, they are likely to be more anxious about him than about later children. Oldest children are weaned later on the average and show stronger emotional reactions to it. Like the only child, the oldest child is exposed for the first part of his life to a triangular situation. As in the one-child family, the father is often unconsciously jealous of the oldest child because the mother's attention is now turned away from him. Coming at a critical period in the formation of the parent-child relationship, this attitude may be preserved even when the child is much older. Oldest children are more likely to be disciplined by the father than are younger siblings, when both parents are present, and the father is more likely to be unusually strict with the oldest child than with later ones.

The oldest child has the inevitable experience of being replaced as the mother's center of attention by a new baby. The result is the phenomenon of sibling rivalry, frequently shown in the form of disguised or open attacks on a younger brother or sister. Perhaps because they understand his feelings, parents put up with this aggressiveness more often in an oldest child than in younger ones.

The younger child in a family of two never undergoes the experience of being replaced. Aside from the attacks of his older sibling, he is likely to lead a relatively sunny and protected early life. However, as he grows older, he is likely to be continually frustrated whenever he comes into competition with his older brother or sister. At the same time, he benefits from what his parents have learned about child rearing through experience with the first child. He also profits from having a person near his own age on whom he can model his own behavior.

Children in a two-child family have the possibility of using relationships between other individuals as a model for their own. For instance, the older child is very likely to try to develop a relationship with the younger sibling similar to that which his parents have developed with him. This is often encouraged by the parents and resisted by the younger child, in about equal measure.

Similarly, the younger child is likely to model his relationships with his parents after those developed by the older child. In this case he often attempts to improve them, and sometimes succeeds.

The many-child family. Beyond the two-child family, the possible variations in family structure become highly complex. Most studies of child behavior lump all of the children between the youngest and oldest as "middle children." Such a classification is overly simple, for the position of the middle child in a three-child family, offering as it does an opportunity for triangle formation, is very different from that of the two middle children in a four-child family, where it is easy to form pairs according to age, sex, or family position. According to Sears and his associates (1957) the middle child in the American families which they studied has more difficulties that either the youngest or the oldest. He receives less atten-

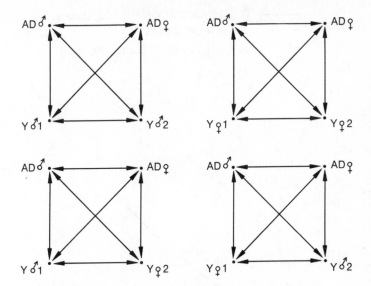

FIGURE 4.4 Combinations of social relationships in two-child families. The children are divided into younger and older individuals, resulting in thirteen kinds of relationships in four combinations.

tion from his mother, less praise for good behavior, and is given more jobs than either the youngest or the oldest child.

Some of the differences in parental behavior that are correlated with differences in the family position of children are given in Table 4.1. Regardless of whether the final results on the children's behavior can be attributed to early or later experience, the effects of family position are certainly long lasting and sometimes serious. For example, it is regularly found that oldest children, and especially the oldest boy in a family, are more likely to have serious emotional problems than are children occupying other family positions.

The effect of family size on the development of social relationships. Each new child added to the family adds a number of relationships which is equal to the previous size of the family. Thus the first child adds two relationships; the second, three; the third, four, and so on. The possible interactions and sources of social stimulation increase in the same way. Consequently, the complexity of family organization increases much more rapidly than it would if the effect were a simple linear one. (See Figure 4-5.) A younger child

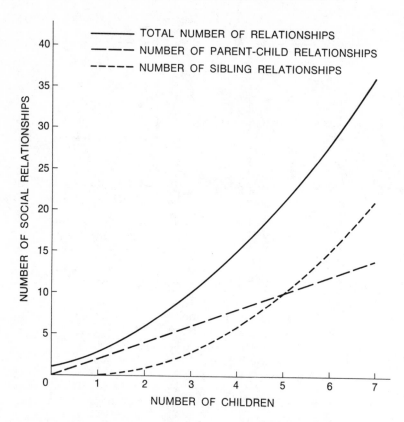

FIGURE 4.5   The effect of family size on the number of social relationships between members of the family.

thus lives in a much richer social environment for the first part of his life than an older one did at the same period.

Each child in the family develops relationships with the same number of mature adults, but the intensity of these relationships and the quantity of time spent in them must inevitably be diluted as the number of children increases, because the parents are usually able to attend to only one child at a time. Consequently, the younger child tends to have a poorer social environment with respect to parental relations and attention (Figure 4.6).

Relationships between the members of a family develop throughout their lives together and even after the family has broken up, being halted only by the death of one or both members of the relationship. We would expect that early experience would have

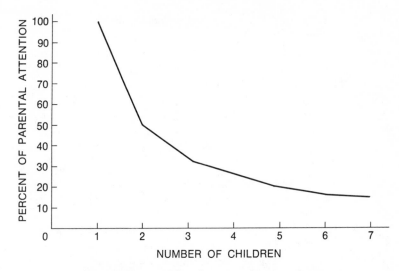

FIGURE 4.6 The division of parental attention in families of different sizes (assuming equal attention to each child). Note the proportionately large decrease between one- and two-child families.

an important effect upon the development of a social relationship within the family, since organization of behavior would take place rapidly at the beginning of the relationship. However, so much development takes place later that we would not expect the relationships to become completely set in the early years. Furthermore, in the experience of most children, it is only the relationships with parents and older siblings that are formed within the first two years, while relationships with younger siblings develop as a part of later rather than early experience.

FAMILY POSITION

Effects on social behavior outside the family. As indicated above, the primary effects of early social experience are felt in the development of social relationships within the family. Rather than studying these primary relationships, most experimenters who have been interested in the results of family organization have tried to study its effects either upon relationships developed outside the family or upon measures of individual behavior which could only be remotely related to the family relationships. For example, Helen Koch (1955,

1956a, 1956b, 1956c) studied the behavior of young children in the Chicago schools as evaluated by their teachers. Since most elementary teachers are women, one would expect that the children, if they generalized at all, would generalize to these strange adults only relationships which they had developed with their mother. Such a study would thus provide no information about the other relationships of the children within the family, and only an indirect reflection of their mother-child relationships.

Aside from this limitation, hers was an unusually complete and well-designed piece of research. By surveying the children in many public schools she was able to locate groups of sixteen children in each of the eight family positions involved in a two-child family. In addition, she divided the children into three groups for each position, according to their relative ages. Group I was separated by less than two years; Group II by two to four years; and Group III, by four to six years; the last being the maximum separation possible for an older child aged six.

The children's teachers rated them on their attitudes toward adults, attitudes toward work, and on their general emotional attitudes. These results were then subjected to an analysis of variance which indicated both the direct effects of the variables (the sex of the child, the sex of his sibling, his rank in the family, and the spacing between him and his sibling), and the effects of combinations of these various factors.

The most striking thing about the results was the importance of sex, both that of the child himself and that of his sibling. In three studies involving a total of thirty ratings, sixteen direct effects were large enough to be considered statistically significant. Eight of these were related to sex and four of them to the sibling's sex. Relative age and age differences had little direct effect. In effects attributed to combinations between different factors, there was no indication that any one of the factors was more often involved than the others.

In general, the differences which teachers noticed in their young pupils' attitudes were mostly related to sex. For example, they saw the girls as more affectionate, more obedient, more responsive to approval, and less resistant to suggestions than boys. Such differences may be true reflections of biological sex differences, or at least of the relationships which female teachers set up with children of opposite sexes, and possibly they reflect characteristics of the original mother-child relationships, but they also correspond to the usual stereotypes of sex roles. If the latter is true, the differences related to the sex of the sibling indicate that some modification of the sex role results from having a sister or brother.

In another part of the experiment, Koch asked the teachers to rate their pupils on the tendencies of girls to act like tomboys and boys to act like sissies. On the average, the ratings were always higher in the case of children who had siblings of the opposite sex. However, the differences that the teachers saw in the children's behavior in school were not great. Boyishness, for instance, did not show statistically significant differences except in younger sisters with much older brothers. Sissyness in the boys decreased as the age difference between them and their sisters increased. Again, this behavior as seen in school by teachers is presumably a somewhat pale reflection of the relationships set up by siblings at home.

By the time students reach college age, there are more profound effects upon behavior resulting from family position and its accompanying organization. Schachter (1959) did an experiment in which he asked girls to subject themselves to electric shock. One group was deliberately frightened beforehand, and the other group was given verbal encouragement. Then the girls were asked whether they would prefer to be alone before the electric shock was given or whether they would prefer to wait with a group. Those girls who had been deliberately frightened by the experimenter tended to choose staying with the group, showing that even in adults isolation is hard to bear. Of the girls who chose to stay with the group, a large proportion were girls who were either only children or the oldest children in their families. Schachter tried to identify those girls who were made highly anxious by the situation, as indicated by their replies to a questionnaire or by their unwillingness to continue the experiment. Of these, 80 per cent of the first-born and only children preferred to stay together, whereas only 30 per cent of the later-born children preferred to do this. Schachter concluded that first-born children become more anxious and fearful and bear pain less well than later born siblings.

In evaluating this experiment, we should remember that the subjects were all girls and therefore that the results do not necessarily apply to boys. Furthermore, the findings are expressed as trends rather than absolute results. Not all oldest or only children become frightened in the experimental situation, nor do all younger children remain calm and prefer to be alone. These trends only partially differentiate individuals in different family positions and may be considerably modified by experience and genetic differences.

Rosenberg and Sutton-Smith (1964) made an extensive study of children in the fourth to sixth grades in fourteen different schools in Northwestern Ohio. Rather than attempting to select equal numbers in each family position, they tested the children as they found them and analyzed the results with respect to sex and ordinal position. Their data give interesting results regarding the prevalence of the two-child family in this region. Out of nine hundred subjects, only twelve boys and seven girls were only children. Likewise, they were able to find only very small numbers of children in three-child families, the numbers ranging from five to nineteen in each of the family positions studied. Their results are therefore most complete with respect to the two-child family.

The children were given several questionnaires, of which the children's form of the Manifest Anxiety Scale gave the most interesting results. This scale can be interpreted as an indication of readiness to admit to and divulge feelings of tension rather than as any indication of hidden tensions. One striking difference shows up between older and younger children when both children are boys. The younger child admits much less anxiety than his older brother. There is no difference between sisters in this respect, and the anxiety scores of children in families of mixed sexes are uniformly high. In all these combinations of siblings, only the younger of two brothers appears to lead a relatively happy life. This result raises two questions: Why is the "happy younger-brother effect" not seen in boys with older sisters, and why is a similar effect not apparent in girls?

We can answer the first question by assuming that the presence of an older child of the opposite sex puts a boy into conflict with the customary sex role for males. He may wish to play with dolls or lipstick like his sister, but he is sternly informed that this behavior is undesirable according to the cultural code. The same thing could theoretically happen to a girl with an older brother, except that girls in our present day society are not severely censured for imitating males.

If there is any generality about the effect of being a youngest child, one would expect that younger girls would also show less anxiety than their older sisters, but this does not appear to be the case. It is possible that girls are allowed such full expression of their fears by our cultural code that the scale simply does not pick up such differences.

The Ohio study also provided some interesting negative results. Family position in these children was not related either to masculinity-feminity scores (an index of conflict over sex-role identification) or to scores of impulsivity (an index of emotional conflict). These findings lead to the encouraging conclusion that relatively few of the children were severely emotionally disturbed by their family position.

Birth order and performance. There is a great deal of evidence to show that in two-child families older children are more likely to achieve eminence or show outstanding performance than their younger siblings. In three-child families the oldest performs best and the youngest is likely to do better than the middle child. These conclusions are supported by such measures of eminence as inclusion in *Who's Who in America,* or high performance on I.Q. tests. The figures usually quoted show that about 64 percent of eminent individuals of this sort from two-child families are older children, as opposed to the 50 percent which might be expected by chance (Altus, 1966).

Such measures of eminence or high performance are affected by large numbers of factors, ranging from family economics (if these are limited, the oldest child is likely to be given more financial support) to the age of the mother at the birth of the child (young mothers are likely to give birth to healthier and more vigorous children). However, the fact that the youngest child in a large family usually does better than the middle children makes it seem likely that one of the most important factors is simply the amount of parental attention and help given to a child.

The general results of all these studies still do not approach some of the basic emotional effects which we might expect from the development of different sorts of primary social relationships. The family environment can vary in many ways, beginning with family size. Freud extensively studied the dynamics of the one-child family, and we are just beginning to get information about the effects of siblings upon each other in two-child families. At present, little information is available on families beyond this size.

The results that we now have from the study of early family environment indicate that objectively measurable effects do occur. However, most of these effects appear to be relatively unimportant, partly because experimenters have not used tests especially designed for the purpose of measuring the kinds of effects which are commonly observed and theoretically expected but have instead used readily accessible, but often inappropriate, tests designed for other purposes. In addition, too little attention has been paid to measuring changes in those social relationships within the family which should be directly affected by its structure and organization.

SUMMARY

The results of early experience in the social environment are difficult to separate from those of later experience. The nature of an experience in early infancy may have relatively little effect in itself but nevertheless lead to a series of consequences whose effects are exerted over many years. The age at which adoption takes place may lead to a very different emotional reaction on the part of the child, and this in turn may result in an emotional attitude on the part of the parents that may last for years. Likewise, the family position into which a child is born affects his social environment not only during early infancy but also for all the years he spends at home and possibly for the rest of his life. Early social experiences therefore represent turning points, as when the process of primary socialization determines which particular individuals will be close social relatives and which will not. They also determine starting points for long continued processes, such as the development of relationships with older and younger siblings.

One of the most important developmental processes in early social experience is that of primary socialization, or imprinting. Every highly social bird or mammal whose development has been analyzed in detail shows a relatively ·short period early in life during which emotional attachments are made, normally with members of the same species. In the human infant this period occurs from approximately six weeks to seven months of age. Children and adults can, of course, develop social attachments at any age but form later ones much less rapidly.

The period of primary socialization is a critical one in that it determines the close social relatives of the individual. Once the emotional bonds are formed, breaking them either temporarily or permanently produces an emotional disturbance of lesser or greater degree, and this complicates the problem of adoption at any age except that prior to or early in the period of primary socialization. Experimental studies of the effects of isolation during the critical period in non-human animals show great disturbances in the socialization process, and it is possible that semi-isolation, which some-times occurs in human infants, has the effect of inducing unusual shyness.

Human families show somewhat unique variation in social experience resulting from differences in family structure and the positions of each child within it. Similar situations probably occur in some other primate groups, but these have been relatively little studied as yet.

The immediate effects of these factors are modifications of the development of social relationships. An only child never develops sibling relationships and therefore never experiences sibling rivalry. However, most studies made in the past have attempted to measure the effects on individual behavior outside the family, rather than the effects on primary social relationships. These indirect effects are often not clear-cut or very large, but several studies indicate that in two-child families the older child tends to become more anxious than the younger one in certain situations not directly involving the other sibling. Among high performers, oldest children out-number younger ones in a ratio approximately two to one, although these differences are not apparent at lower levels of performance. It would seem that oldest children are likely to become more highly motivated than younger ones, and especially more than middle children, probably because they receive greater amounts of parental attention than the others. Their greater feelings of anxiety may thus be a by-product of high motivation.

5 EFFECTS OF EARLY EXPERIENCE ON SOCIAL BEHAVIOR

In the last chapter, we saw that variation in the early social environment produces drastic changes in behavioral development, especially through the modification of the process of primary socialization. Disturbances of the process produce immediate and violent emotional reactions, and the nature of the experience during the critical period for primary socialization determines much of the organization of social behavior in later life. In this chapter we shall look more closely at some of the consequences of early social experience. These long-range effects may involve a simple transference of social behavior patterns to inappropriate objects or individuals, or they may involve extensive modification of these patterns even to the point of complete suppression. They especially involve the organization of social behavior between individuals, with the consequent modification of social relationships.

Most of the results which we shall discuss here are derived from experiments on animals other than human beings. There are two reasons for this approach. One is the difficulty of getting any clear-cut results with human beings. The other is that experiments with a variety of species point to certain general implications which would be impossible to derive from the study of one species alone.

Such implications are hypotheses that should be accepted only if they can actually be verified by observation and experiment. One can never generalize directly from one species to another, since even the most general phenomena may be modified by the peculiar heredity and social organization of the species concerned. Many of the major implications from infrahuman animal experiments either have not or cannot be tested on people because of possible serious consequences. The human data have been extensively reviewed elsewhere, and the interested reader may consult these works and with their help attempt to chart his way through a maze of contradictory results and tentative conclusions.

CARE SOLICITING-BEHAVIOR

Many young mammals are born in such a helpless state that they can perform very few activities for themselves. Consequently, some sort of calling or signaling for care and attention is very common. This behavior is an adaptive substitute for food getting, for comfort seeking, and for adaptations to threats or attacks. In other words, care-soliciting behavior is the infantile substitute for many patterns of behavior belonging to the ingestive, agonistic, and shelter-seeking behavioral systems. In animals that show allelomimetic behavior, care soliciting may also substitute for it in that signaling keeps the infant in contact with other animals.

Distress vocalization in dogs. One of the first reactions of a new-born puppy is a high-pitched whining or yelping, which results from hunger, cold, or pain. If the mother is successful in meeting the needs of her puppies, they rapidly become more and more quiet. The rate of vocalization also declines with age. In one experiment we counted the number of vocalizations given by puppies while they were being weighed. The rate, which was highest at birth, declined almost to zero by four weeks of age.

Beginning at about three weeks, puppies begin to vocalize at high rates in strange situations and when isolated from familiar individuals. This reaction, which seems to be caused by the absence of the familiar rather than by fear of the strange, stays at a high level until about eight weeks, shortly after the time of final weaning from the breast, and declines rapidly thereafter, although it never entirely disappears, even in adult dogs. This emotional reaction is closely associated with the development of allelomimetic behavior, since it has the effect of making the animal uncomfortable when apart from familiar individuals.

Crying. The behavior of human infants which corresponds to distress vocalization in the puppy is crying. Like the puppy, the helpless human infant employs it as a substitute for several of the adult behavioral systems, and as he grows older he tends to cry less often, just as the puppy grows quieter with age, although the capacity is never competely lost in either species. Crying in response to discomfort and hunger appears at birth, and crying in strange situations first occurs about two months of age at the beginning of the period of socialization.

There are several experimental studies dealing with the development and decline of crying in certain situations. Levy (1960) recorded the frequency of crying at medical examinations, finding that there was almost no crying in babies less than two months old, and that it rose to a peak around two years, declining rapidly thereafter. Two years is also the time when the child first starts to talk in sentences and also begins to be able to understand verbal explanation. The implications are that this is the age when children first begin to gain verbal understanding of situations and substitute verbal appeals for help in place of purely emotional ones.

Tail wagging in dogs. About the same time that the puppy begins to vocalize in the absence of familiar companions, it also begins to react in a positive way to their presence. At three weeks, or a little before, the puppy gives its first tentative tail wags, which soon develop into the rapid horizontal wagging that signals a more or less friendly and submissive attitude. The frequency of tail wagging rises rapidly until it reaches its maximum when the puppy is about five weeks of age. The rate remains high in juvenile animals and declines somewhat in adults. This is a behavior pattern which appears early in development, lasts throughout life, and has only one simple function—that of communicating a social emotion. In the human infant there is a corresponding behavior pattern which has almost exactly the same characteristics: the social smile. The only difference is that one looks at the other end of the infant for the signal.

Smiling. The first social smile of a young baby is one of the best indicators that the process and period of primary socialization has begun. Although smiling can be elicited by anything resembling a human face, experience also has an effect upon its frequency, even in early infancy. Children who are reared by their own mothers smile more often at her than at other individuals during the first six months of life, while babies reared in orphanages are more indiscriminate (Ambrose, 1961). Smiling to a stranger develops later in orphanage babies and reaches a peak later than in family reared infants (Gewirtz, 1965). Food rewards have little effect on smiling, but social reinforcement such as talking or picking the child up will change the rate of the smiling response (Brackbill, 1958). Whether or not early experience affects smiling in later life is unknown, but since this behavior is used as an important tool for communication and influencing the behavior of both adults and children, it is very possible that early experience may have some lasting effects.

INGESTIVE BEHAVIOR

Sucking. An infant mammal at first obtains all of its nourishment in liquid form by means of sucking, and one of the problems raised by this behavior is whether a physical or emotional need for sucking exists apart from nutrition itself. Attempts to raise young rats by tube feeding result in a high death rate from hard curd in the stomach, and this can be prevented by allowing them to nurse on a dry female. Sucking is apparently necessary to stimulate the peristaltic movements of the stomach. Other young mammals are less seriously affected when not allowed to suck. Calves or lambs can be taught to drink their milk almost from birth and suffer no ill effects, and puppies can be reared by tube feeding without great difficulty.

There have been several attempts to determine whether the ability to suck will persist in the absence of early experience. It is dif-

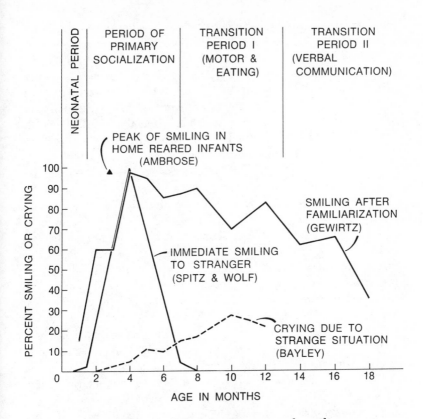

FIGURE 5.1 The development of smiling and crying in human infants, in relation to periods of development. The peak of the smiling response to a strange face occurs at about four months and is characteristic of the period of primary socialization, during which the first social attachments are formed.

ficult to be sure that an infant animal has never sucked, even with careful dropper or tube feeding, but the evidence is that a young puppy will readily suck at the first opportunity at any time before the normal age of weaning. Young kittens will readily change to new sucking objects, such as a brooder, at any time up until about six weeks of age, which again is near the time of normal weaning (Schneirla and Rosenblatt, 1961). All this indicates that the capacity to suck needs no postnatal experience for its development and that it will persist for long periods without being used. Does it also mean that a young animal needs oral stimulation?

Becoming interested in the problem of sucking because of its relation to psychoanalytic theory, the psychiatrist David M. Levy (1934) reared a litter of puppies on the bottle, feeding them on a regular schedule like human babies and giving some of them nipples with large holes and some with small. He found that the pups which he had fed through small-holed nipples requiring more sucking did less sucking on a human finger when given the opportunity. He concluded that the puppies had a need for sucking apart from the nutrition it produces.

Puppies spontaneously show an equivalent of human thumb sucking (sucking each other's paws, tails, and genitalia) if they have been weaned early but never show it if normally nursed by the mother. We (Scott., et al 1959) did an experiment with the effects of early weaning at different ages, and found that up until the age of nineteen or twenty days but not later, hunger would cause these early weaned puppies to suck more on a human finger; all these puppies were fed frequently and ad lib, and none developed the practice of sucking the tails or paws of their litter mates which corresponds to human thumb sucking. However, puppies that were weaned early and then fed on a regular schedule twice a day showed tail sucking no matter whether they were overfed or underfed (Elliot and King, 1960). These experiments show that the phenomenon of excessive non-nutritive sucking is dependent upon several factors. Of these, the age of the infant and, in particular, the degree of motivation which is aroused by either hunger or learned motivation resulting from scheduled feeding appear to be most important. If these results can be extended to human infants, one way to avoid thumb sucking would be to avoid rigidly scheduled feeding.

Scheduled feedings are a regular part of institutional life. Kunst (1948) studied the thumb and finger sucking of 143 infants reared in a Chicago orphanage by touring the wards at ten-minute intervals and observing which infants were sucking. Every baby did some non-nutritive sucking, and under some circumstances as many as sixty percent of them were seen sucking their thumbs or fingers. For the schedule-fed baby, thumb sucking would appear to be a normal way of life.

The rate of sucking was low at birth and rose during the first three months of life, falling off slightly after supplementary feeding was begun and rising again after final weaning from the bottle. The sucking rate went up in proportion to the time since the most recent feeding, and this increase was especially marked in babies over three months of age. Non-nutritive sucking is obviously related to hunger, which scheduled feeding intensifies through a process of conditioning. When scheduled feedings are separated by long intervals they also have the effect of prolonging hunger.

Sucking is also related to sleep, as older babies suck nearly twice as often when asleep. It is possible that many babies learn to control awareness of hunger pangs by inducing sleep through sucking. If so, thumb sucking is a mildly neurotic method of emotional control.

Other than the annoyance to spectators, the effect of thumb sucking on future behavior is probably slight. Sucking behavior has

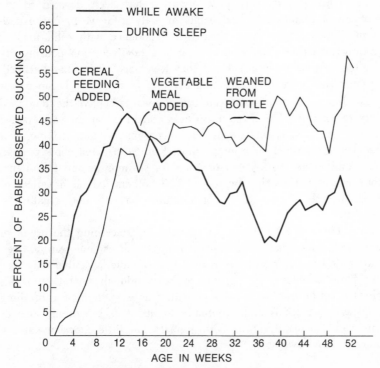

FIGURE 5.2 The development of finger- and thumb-sucking in babies fed on a regular schedule. (Smoothed curves from data by Kunst.)

been evolved to function chiefly in the neonatal period. As we have seen in earlier chapters, there is a general tendency among non-pre-cocious mammals toward behavioral evolution in two directions, one leading to behavior patterns useful in the neonatal period, when most of the animal's needs are provided by parental care, and the other leading to the perfection of behavior patterns useful in adult life. Since the two kinds of behavior have been produced by evolution in different directions, they need not be functionally related to each other. The implication is that experiential effects on infantile be-havior may affect it alone and not necessarily lead to effects on adult forms of behavior. Thus it may not make much difference whether a human infant obtains his food by breast, bottle, or cup feeding, as long as he survives to the point where he can feed himself (Sears, et al, 1953).

Eating. Relatively little attention has been devoted to the problem of establishing food habits in early infancy. In one experi-ment, puppies were given their first experience with solid food as feedings of either ground horse meat or a relatively unappetizing dry dog food. At eleven weeks of age, they were each given the other food. Puppies that were used to eating dry dog food readily began to eat meat, but those that had been eating meat accepted the dog food very reluctantly. This experiment was concluded at an early period in life, and the results might have been much more striking if it had been continued for a longer time. Kuo (1967) fed chow puppies on a limited diet of soybean products for six months and found that they would not touch new foods, while others fed on a variety of foods in early life would accept anything that was not actually dis-tasteful.

There is a great deal of speculation concerning the origin of undesirable food habits in human beings, such as undereating, over-eating, and undue restriction of diet. For example, a mother may feed her child whenever he appears to be emotionally upset, and this practice could lead to a habit of eating as a method of controlling unpleasant emotions and eventually to obesity. Hypotheses such as this could be readily tested with animals, but little experimental evi-dence is now available.

ELIMINATIVE BEHAVIOR

Many mammals which live in dens or lairs have behavior pat-terns that provide for sanitation. In neonatal puppies, urination and defecation are elicited as reflexes in reaction to licking by the mother and normally never occur without such stimulation. Later the puppies develop strong inhibitions against defecating or urinating while asleep or in the sleeping place. The result is that the nest or den is always clean.

The reactions of cats to sand boxes is well known, and many rodents that live in burrows have certain areas which are used as latrines. In contrast, primates like howling monkeys sleep in trees, rarely stay long in one spot while feeding, and show no behavior patterns regulating elimination, except that they are more likely to urinate or defecate when disturbed. Housebreaking a monkey is a difficult or almost impossible process, as it has no behavior patterns which meet this adaptive function.

Few of the animal experiments on eliminative behavior can be applied to man because no other species has similar behavior patterns. We can speculate about the adaptive problems of precultural man, but all that we know definitely is that men. have been ground-living primates since the remote past, and we can therefore assume that their behavior has evolved toward life in these conditions. Certainly all modern men have definite sleeping places, and keeping these clean is a universal sanitary problem. Unlike dogs or cats, the human infant seems to have no behavior that would be conducive to sanitation, and this leaves the solution of the sanitation problem entirely up to the behavior of the parents. This being the case, no adaptive value would result from the infant's developing control of elimination before the age when he was able to crawl or walk away from his sleeping place. Even if bladder and bowel release were evolved as a response to being picked up and carried, the baby would be very likely to relieve himself in the sleeping place, rather than waiting until he was carried outside. These theoretical considerations lead to the conclusion that toilet training should not be seriously undertaken until the child is about a year and a half old and able to manage his own locomotion.

Using this approach, Brazelton (1962) has reported the results of recommending to parents that they not begin toilet training until an even later age, when their children were two years old. The reports from over a thousand cases indicated that children who were not toilet trained until they were two achieved continence slightly later on the average than did children who were started earlier, but with about four month's less effort. Furthermore, only about two percent of the children showed bed wetting, constipation, and similar problems at the age of five, as opposed to the ten to twenty percent that pediatricians usually find in their practice.

The physiology of elimination. The internal activities involved in elimination are highly complex, involving both voluntary and involuntary control. The contraction of the bladder during urination is involuntary, but the contraction of its sphincter muscle is voluntary. At the same time, relaxation of this muscle is not entirely voluntary. Both kinds of control are subject to conditioning, and this is one way to bring involuntary behavior indirectly under voluntary control. Thus many people are able to induce urination through the sound of running water, presumably because the sound is similar to that of urination.

In the case of defecation, the contraction of the anal sphincter muscle is under voluntary control. However, the contractions of the colon, which are necessary for elimination, are involuntary, and unless they occur defecation is difficult or impossible. Conversely, the sphincter muscle may not be able to overcome strong colonic contractions. These contractions can be conditioned with respect to the time of day, but one of the most effective methods of bringing this behavior under control is through the gastro-colic reflex. Contractions of the colon are stimulated by the presence of food in the stomach, so that bowel movements have a tendency to occur after meal times.

The task of a mother in toilet training is to condition not only the voluntary behavior of the child but also his internal involuntary reactions. Since eliminative behavior lasts all through life, the way in which the mother does the training may have long-lasting consequences with respect to physical comfort, particularly if she uses too severe inhibitory training. The result of this is either to make elimination difficult under certain circumstances or to make bed wetting more common. There is no good objective evidence that the mode or severity of toilet training has a general effect upon the adult personality, although such a result has been advanced as a theoretical possibility. It is more likely that the mode of toilet training reflects a general attitude toward child training on the part of the parents that would have an influence over a much longer period of life than would their behavior in the toilet-training age alone.

INVESTIGATIVE BEHAVIOR AND COMFORT-SEEKING BEHAVIOR

Investigative behavior is a basic part of problem solving. As will be shown in the next chapter, restriction of the physical environment and of stimulation during early life will reduce exploratory and investigatory activity. This reduction results in part from fearful reactions to strange situations, and in part from extending a habit of not investigating formed in an environment where nothing is new.

Comfort-seeking behavior is also strongly related to the conditions of the physical environment. While much experimental work has been done with the effect of discomfort in early life, little attention has been paid to the modification of comfort-seeking activities in later existence. Would uncomfortable experiences in early infancy lead an animal or a person to seek out a comfortable existence in adult life, or would he, on the contrary, accept discomfort more readily?

ALLELOMIMETIC BEHAVIOR

This activity may be defined as doing the same thing as other individuals, with some degree of mutual stimulation. It is a highly important kind of behavior for social animals that live in mobile groups, and examples can be seen in flocks of birds, herds of hoofed mammals, and groups of primates, as well as in many other species.

As stated above, the development of allelomimetic behavior in an animal like a dog is associated with the appearance of an emotional reaction to being isolated, expressed in vocalizations that are the canine equivalent of crying. The young puppy must very soon learn that this emotion is produced by being apart from the group and is relieved by staying with it. This rather simple emotional mechanism thus provides the physiological basis for the behavior.

The expression of this behavior is highly susceptible to experimental modification. In the dog, rearing a young puppy in isolation during the critical period for socialization effectively prevents the development of allelomimetic behavior. Puppies separated and reared in this way later move and play in competely solitary ways even when they are permanently replaced together and confined in the same pen. If, on the other hand, a young puppy is taken from other dogs at a comparable age and raised entirely with people, it will develop allelomimetic behavior entirely with the human group and be almost completely indifferent to other dogs.

Similar experiments can be done with sheep, where allelomimetic behavior is even more highly developed. Normally the young lamb follows its mother on every occasion, and a flock of sheep when alarmed will all rush together and then move off in a direction determined by one of the older members of the flock. For the flock to function effectively, the tendency toward allelomimetic behavior must gradually decline in later maturity, so that the older and more experienced members will act independently and be followed by the others.

The development of this kind of behavior has been little studied in human beings except in the highly symbolic form of "conformity," and the following remarks are therefore somewhat hypothetical. Allelomimetic behavior can only appear after the baby is able to walk, at approximately fifteen months of age, on the average. However, at this early stage, walking is so ineffective that real imitation and following is impossible, and the first signs of true allelomimetic behavior are more likely to show up at two years, or even later.

As to its emotional basis, there is evidence that babies begin to show fear reactions to strange places at about two months of age and fear of strangers at about six months. By the time they can talk, children begin to show fear of being alone in the dark. As with other social animals, children must soon learn that being alone is unpleasant and staying with others and doing what they do is pleasant. This kind of behavior is of course reinforced by conscious training. The young child who leaves its parents and runs out into the street alone is likely to be punished, and with good reason.

The reduction of allelomimetic behavior with age is similar in both human development and in that of other animals; allelomimetic behavior is highly advantageous for the survival of the young, but independence is also essential for later life and must be developed as the individual grows older.

In dogs, puppies are normally taken from their mothers and litter mates at about the time of final weaning from the breast. The result is a strong emotional reaction to separation, and dogs experimentally treated in this way develop strong attachments, greater dependency, and hence prolonged allelomimetic behavior in connection with their human foster-relatives.

Such drastic experiments as these are of course never performed on human infants, but the circumstances of family living may bring about individual differences, as we have seen in Chapter 4. When threatened, the older sister in a family of two is more likely to seek safety in a group than her younger sister. Neither overdependence nor overconformity is desirable, and the ideal course of development is one in which a child learns both the pleasures of acting in concert with others and the usefulness of independent action under appropriate conditions.

AGONISTIC BEHAVIOR

Fighting. A great many experimental studies indicate that early experience strongly influences agonistic behavior. Most of the highly social animals that live in groups for long periods have developed ways of controlling destructive fighting within their ranks. One method is the process of early socialization, which produces close social bonds between young animals before they are able to fight. They thus form strong habits of not fighting with each other and continue these habits as they grow older. Male house mice begin to fight strange mice sometime between thirty-two and thirty-six days of age, when the male hormone first becomes active. However, if they are raised together from birth, they may not begin to fight until long after maturity and, even then, the fights may not be severe (Scott, 1966). The behavioral mechanism involved is simply that of passive inhibition, or associating a particular situation with the absence of a certain kind of behavior. There is every reason to expect that a similar developmental mechanism exists in children.

Another general type of social control is the development of a dominance order. Young puppies reared together will begin to show playful fighting during the period of socialization. Even if relatively severe fights occur, they are usually settled without serious damage, because at this age both teeth and motor coordination are so undeveloped that it is difficult for the puppies to hurt each other very much. As a result, the puppies work out habitual modes of behavior in any situation of conflict, in which the dominant animal threatens and the subordinate one submits, but no actual fighting takes place.

Similar playful fights break out between both young rhesus monkeys and baboons. When this happens the most dominant male in the group is likely to move toward the young fighters in a threatening and impressive way, thus breaking up the fight before any damage can be done. This behavior also has the effect of establishing the place of the young monkeys in the dominance hierarchy before they have the capacity to engage in serious fights. As a result, serious fighting very rarely occurs within a naturally formed group.

A dominance relationship can also be established without the use of overt threats or punishment. In one experiment with puppies, (Scott and Fuller, 1965) we reared them without punishment of any kind. For the purposes of the experiment we began handling them from the day of their birth, in order to place them in various test and measuring situations. The result was that the puppies became completely subordinate and could be controlled at any time by picking them up. When approached as adults, they would flatten out and assume subordinate postures, and we could even break up an incipient fight by picking up the contestants, who almost immediately drooped passively in our arms. Over a period of several years, none of these dogs attempted to rebel or bite. It is quite possible that the usual methods of caring for human infants, who are repeatedly picked up and carried throughout a long period of infancy, have the same effect of establishing a strong dominance order of parents over children.

Although the dominance order works efficiently to prevent fighting within an animal group, it has little or no effect on behavior exhibited toward animals outside the group. Animals which are completely peaceable within their own group may be highly aggressive toward strangers.

What happens when an individual grows up without any opportunity to develop the usual controls over agonistic behavior? A young puppy reared in complete isolation from three until sixteen weeks of age—and thus left without social contact during the entire period of primary socialization—has no experience with playful fighting. When he is introduced to normally reared puppies, they react to him as a stranger and frequently begin to attack. He will respond defensively but is, of course, at a great disadvantage, and he usually loses. If he is placed with another puppy that has been reared in isolation, the two animals pay little attention to each other and never fight. The absence of the opportunity for playful fighting can thus result in the complete suppression of the appearance of fighting behavior, even though the capacity is still present.

The effects are especially striking in fox terriers, a breed which has been selected for its capacity to develop aggressiveness and endure pain. If raised with their mother and litter mates, these puppies will get into serious fights by the time they are seven weeks old. In most cases, they cannot be reared in groups larger than three animals. In contrast, the fox-terrier puppy that has been reared in isolation during the period of socialization is completely indifferent to others unless he is attacked.

Escape and fearful behavior. Most animals show certain fearful responses without previous experience. Usually, these are general in nature, such as fear of falling, loud noises, and sudden movements. Similar fearful reactions can be found in human babies in addition to the fearful reaction to strange situations which develops as soon as the infant is capable of discriminating between strange and familiar surroundings.

As animals grow older, they develop more specialized fear responses, and these can be experimentally shown to result from special experiences. Sheep are almost universally afraid of dogs. A bottle-reared lamb, however, will ordinarily be completely indifferent to dogs, or sometimes even be attracted by them if he is raised in the same household. As adults, such pet sheep are very likely to fall victims to marauding dogs which attack the flock.

Similarly, one would expect human infants to learn specific fears as a result of experience. Deliberately frightening a baby for experimental purposes might have dangerous results and has seldom been done. However, Levy (1960) observed babies as they were brought into the doctor's office to receive inoculations and found that at 6 months of age they began to show fear of the needle which had previously hurt them. As many parents know, such an early fear reinforced many times in later childhood can become quite serious in an older child, whose reaction to injections may be out of proportion to the actual pain involved.

SEXUAL BEHAVIOR

Sexual behavior ordinarily appears in its complete form only at sexual maturity. However, most of the higher animals exhibit some playful sex behavior long before this time. In precocious mammals like sheep, playful mounting can be seen within the first ten days of life, and in the puppy it appears early in the period of socialization.

Effects of cross-fostering. If young turkeys are hatched in an incubator and reared by hand entirely away from other birds, they become imprinted (or socialized to) the human handler. As adults, such turkey males will show the usual courtship mating behavior with other females. However, as soon as a human being enters the scene, the males desert the turkey females and attempt to court the person (Schein, 1963). The result of the early experience has not been to change the form of the behavior but to influence the choice of the object toward which it is directed. Such results are typical of those found in hand-reared birds and mammals.

Effects of isolation. The effects of rearing an animal in isolation depend somewhat upon the species concerned. As we have seen, a male Indian jungle fowl raised to maturity in a solitary cage, but able to see outside, has a tendency as an adult to go through the typical courtship dance, or waltzing, but to direct it toward himself rather than toward another bird. Such a bird spins in a circle, futilely pursuing his own tail (Kruijt, 1964).

Harlow and his associates at the University of Wisconsin attempted to rear infant rhesus monkeys apart from their mothers and found that they survived very poorly unless provided with an inanimate model to which they could cling (Harlow and Harlow, 1965). Also, infants reared with these "model mothers" are as adults unable to mate with each other and are seldom successful even when paired with experienced animals (Mason, 1963). The pattern of mating in this species is quite complicated, the female standing quietly on all fours while the male stands on her ankles, and monkeys reared in isolation are unable to coordinate their efforts in this fashion. However, if young monkeys otherwise reared in isolation are allowed a few minutes of daily playful contact with each other sexual behavior develops normally.

Similarly, chimpanzees reared by hand appear to be unable to mate except with experienced animals. The mating behavior of isolated male dogs is also adversely affected. Some of them are able to mate normally, but others remain unsuccessful even after numerous contacts with receptive females (Beach, 1965).

Effects of inhibitory training. Young puppies begin sexual behavior early in the period of socialization, mounting other puppies and nosing their genitalia. Kuo (1967) trained a group of eight male chow puppies to attack other male puppies. They lived together with adult females, but any sort of playful sexual behavior that they showed was punished. When fully grown, these puppies would attack and chase away other males approaching females in heat, but showed no sign of sexual behavior themselves. When we consider the usual strong sexual reactions of male dogs, this result is a convincing demonstration of the effect of early inhibitory training on later sexual behavior.

Such results confirm the impressions from clinical data that strong early inhibitory training can have important effects on sexual behavior in human beings. The concept of infant sexuality proclaimed by Freud is readily confirmed by observation. Male babies will show erections at absurdly early ages, and it is obvious that both boy and girl babies obtain pleasure from contact with their genitalia. Although experimental data are lacking, it is very likely that over-conscientious parents have in the past severely punished their children for actions which appeared to be sexual, and there is every reason to expect that the effects of such inhibitory training might be long lasting.

CARE-GIVING BEHAVIOR

In most mammals care-giving behavior appears only in adults after the birth of their offspring, although in some primates juveniles sometimes appear to care for infants, and immature wolves will feed cubs by vomiting. Nevertheless, care-giving parental activities can be affected by early experience.

Effect of cross-fostering. In many species hand-reared females have a tendency to neglect their offspring. For example, a female lamb that we bottle-reared would allow her own offspring to nurse but did not call them when they strayed away nor did she respond to their calls. The result of her early experience was that she was more responsive to another species than to her own, even including her own offspring.

Effect of isolation. Isolated rhesus monkeys are defective not only in adult mating behavior but in maternal care (Harlow and Harlow, 1965). When, with great efforts, females raised in isolation are successfully mated and produce their own young, they tend to be neglectful and rejecting. The mother is apparently disturbed by the cries of her young infant but responds inappropriately, pushing it away or even striking it. The appropriate behavior of clasping the young infant is apparently learned in the course of play with other young animals. However, the isolated females show considerable powers of recovery as adults and become much better mothers to second infants.

Human care-giving behavior. Such drastic experiments are not done with human infants and are rarely duplicated by accident. Any care-giving behavior shown by young children is almost universally rewarded rather than punished, with the result that we have almost no data concerning the effect of early experience on this type of human behavior. Very large differences in the maternal behavior of women can be observed, ranging from rejection to overprotection

(Levy, 1943), but how much of this behavior is caused by heredity and how much is related to early experience is still a matter of conjecture.

PLAY BEHAVIOR

Play is often a puzzle to psychologists—especially to those with a mechanistic turn of mind—because of its apparent lack of function. However, the above paragraphs should sufficiently indicate that the playful behavior of young mammals has a highly important function in the development of adult patterns of social behavior and social organization. This function is particularly evident in the development of dominance organization in connection with agonistic behavior and in the maturation of the adult patterns of sexual and care-giving behavior. Play behavior may also contribute to the development of allelomimetic behavior, as many of the "running games" of young lambs appear to have this function.

In addition, play undoubtedly contributes to the development of bones and muscles through physical exercises and to the acquisition of motor skills. Animals reared in restricted environments grow nearly as large as free-living ones, but their muscles are less well developed and they are usually deficient in motor coordination.

SUMMARY

Social behavior and organization can be drastically altered by early experience. These changes are brought about in two ways, by direct effects as social behavior appears in early development, and by indirect effects on later behavior. The earliest effects may be highly important either because they set in motion a chain of events which cannot be easily altered later, or because they determine the nature of behavioral organization. On the other hand, they may affect behavior that is important only in early infancy and thus have a limited effect.

Two kinds of behavior are especially important in early infancy. One of these is sucking at the breast, the neonatal form of ingestive behavior; and various distortions of this behavior, chiefly in the direction of non-nutritional sucking, can be produced. Since the function of sucking is soon taken over by the adult form of ingestive behavior, its possible distortions probably have significant effects on later behavior in only a few cases. The other kind of behavior chiefly found in infancy is care soliciting, which includes the distress vocalization of many young mammals and birds and, of course, the crying of human infants. This behavior, however, functions as a substitute for more permanent behavioral systems and is chiefly interesting as it indicates their presence in immature form.

Other behavioral systems appear in early infancy but persist into later life. Among these is the adult form of ingestive behavior. Early experience should have a strong influence on later food preferences, but we have little experimental evidence to this effect. The adult form of eliminative behavior varies widely among different species of animals, both in time of appearance and degree of control. Because human beings have relatively unfixed and late-appearing patterns of bowel and bladder control, proper training methods are an important practical problem, and over-severe training may produce pathological conditions later. Two other behavioral systems appear in the early development of most animals, investigative and comfort-seeking behavior. However, since the function of these systems are closely related to the physical environment, we shall consider them in the next chapter.

The sexual, agonistic, and allelomimetic behavioral systems usually appear somewhat later 'and only in playful forms. In mammals other than primates, care-giving behavior usually does not appear until the animals are completely adult and become parents. The results of early experience upon these kinds of behavior are therefore different but in many cases no less drastic, for there is good evidence that the development of adult patterns of social behavior in many species depends upon the opportunity for play with other young animals.

The general effects of early experience on social behavior take many forms. The frequency of a behavior pattern such as an aggressive attack may vary from zero to an inordinately high rate, depending upon early experience. The development of a behavior pattern may be distorted to the extent that it becomes non-functional, as in the mating behavior of rhesus monkeys. The speed of development of adult behavior patterns may be slowed down or speeded up. Finally, early experience has major effects on the organization of social behavior between individuals, determining those individuals who will become close social relations or strangers, as well as the nature of relationships. In sexual and agonistic behavior, early experience determines the nature and effectiveness of social control.

Since most experimental results come from other animals than human beings and since results vary from species to species, the effects of early experience on the later social behavior and organization of the human species must be inferred either from the nature of human development or from those observations which can be correlated with variations in the early environment. As we have seen earlier, all the major systems of social behavior occur in some form in early human experience. Some of these forms are immature and others only playful, but they are all susceptible to direct modification. Although human beings are rarely subjected to the drastic modifications of early social behavior that can be brought about in experimental animals, there is much clinical evidence that sexual and agonistic behavior can be either badly distorted or allowed to develop normally by the circumstances of early experience and parental care.

6 STIMULATION, PRACTICE, AND ENRICHMENT

As indicated in the previous chapter, the most important part of the environment of a new-born baby or other mammal is the social environment. The human infant is almost completely helpless, and its survival depends upon constant care and protection. However, even at this early age, the baby has some contact with the purely physical environment: heat and cold, pressure and pain, light and dark, sound and silence. In addition, the stimuli received from social sources are purely physical in nature and can be studied as such.

THE EFFECTS OF SENSORY
STIMULATION UPON THE DEVELOPMENT
OF SENSORY CAPACITIES

Physical forces are always impinging upon any living organism, and the chemical composition of the physical environment continually changes. These forces and changes in turn act upon the sense organs to produce internal physio-chemical changes that act as behavioral stimuli. We ordinarily take such stimulation for granted, and it is only when it is drastically altered by experiment or accident that we can detect its effects upon behavorial development. As we saw in Chapter 3, an embryonic mammal is strongly protected from stimulation by the body of its mother, and even after birth maternal care shelters it from extreme environmental changes. A young organism is further blocked off from environmental stimulation by the imperfect development of its sense organs; a newborn kitten can receive only very reduced and diffuse light through its closed eyelids.

However, the young animal is never completely isolated from physical and chemical changes. Even before the development of its sense organs, environmental changes can alter physiological reactions; a notable example being the effect of heat upon the rate of chemical reactions. Furthermore, we are now beginning to accumulate evidence that certain kinds of environmental stimulation are necessary in early life for normal behavioral development. Most of the experimental work has been done with visual and tactile stimulation, although it is well known that congenitally deaf persons have great difficulty in learning to talk, and if not given attention develop into the "deaf-mutes" of an older day.

Visual stimulation. The chimpanzee has sensory capacities very similar to those of human beings and, of all primates, follows a course of behavorial development most similar to that of man. Working at the Yerkes Laboratory in Florida, Riesen (1961a) reared several infant chimpanzees in various conditions of light and darkness. If they were raised in complete darkness, the result was degeneration of the ganglion cells of the retina, as well as biochemical changes in these tissues. One of the animals which was removed from the dark at twelve weeks made a complete recovery; another removed at seven months made a partial recovery; but one left in darkness for a year showed extensive and permanent loss of ganglion cells. Riesen concluded that the retina, like many other nervous tissues, did not develop properly in the absence of stimulation. Function is necessary for development in postnatal life as well as in embryology, where the principle of functional differentiation or adaptation has long been known. While most organs develop to a considerable degree before they become functional, their final form is affected by use. An embryonic vein or artery filled with circulating blood develops quite differently from an empty one.

Because chimpanzees are so expensive and difficult to raise, Riesen (1961b) next turned his attention to cats, as a mother cat can be trusted to rear her offspring efficiently in complete darkness. Kittens reared in the dark did not show the cell degeneration seen in chimpanzees but did show comparable biochemical changes in the retina. The effects were thus less severe but confirmed the need for stimulation as a basis for proper development.

This brought up the problem of determining whether these experiences of visual deprivation had any effect upon behavior as well as upon the sense organs themselves. Several ingenious methods were used to answer this question. In normal development a kitten's eyes open at approximately ten days of age, and between eleven and sixteen days it will first show "tactile placing"; that is, if a kitten is held so that its paw touches a flat surface it will put its paw down as if it were going to walk on it. Between twenty-two and twenty-eight days, it will first show "visual placing" by extending its paw before it actually touches the surface. Riesen raised kittens normally until they were eighteen days of age and then placed them in the dark for twenty-three hours a day. While they were in the light, half the kittens had their heads covered with a fine cloth bag so that only diffuse light entered. This was enough to produce normal biochemical development of the retina. All the kittens were tested for visual placing each day. Naturally, the hooded animals showed no reaction, and their heads were not uncovered until their littermates responded. Five hours later, all of them developed visual placing. This experiment shows that the experience of deprivation of visual stimulation will produce direct effects on behavioral development in addition to those produced indirectly by physiological alteration of the sense organs. The effects in this case were not very drastic, since the period of deprivation was short and the kittens still young when restored to normal life.

A second device for testing the development of visual capacities is the "visual cliff" devised by Walk and Gibson (1961). In this apparatus the subject moves over a glass plate covering two surfaces, one immediately below the plate and another two or three feet lower, with an abrupt edge between. Kittens begin to avoid the edge of the "cliff" at about four weeks of age, and so do young rats.

If rats are raised for four weeks in complete darkness, they respond immediately to the visual cliff as soon as they are brought out into the light. However, when cats are subjected to the same treatment, they show no response at first, and it is only after a week of living in the light that they show the same fear response as kittens which have been reared in the light from the beginning. The different reactions of the two species are associated with different habits of rearing the young. Wild rats are largely nocturnal animals and normally rear their young in complete darkness within nests built in holes. Cats, on the other hand, are adapted for hunting both in daylight and in darkness and begin to bring their kittens out of seclusion for longer and longer periods of play at quite an early age.

The absence of visual stimulation will thus inhibit the development of the capacity for visually discriminating between different depths, at least in the cat. Experiments with total visual deprivation have not of course been carried out with human infants, nor is the visual-cliff apparatus a good one for determining the course of development of their early visual capacities. The experimental method depends upon the baby's making a choice. When he is placed at the edge of the visual cliff and then called by his mother, first from one side and then the other, he will readily come to her across the shallow side but will not cross the deep side. Since babies ordinarily do not begin crawling until six or seven months of age, no experiments have been done with younger infants. By the time they can crawl, babies are well able to distinguish between the two sides of the visual cliff, and other evidence indicates that the capacity for visual pattern discrimination has developed some time before.

A third response which can be used for studying the development of visual capacities is that of visual fixation. Young animals which have their eyes open appear to look at objects selectively and for different periods of time. Fantz (1965) developed a method for measuring this response in the infant chimpanzees of the Yerkes Laboratory, where they were reared much like human babies.

The cornea of the vertebrate eye acts as a mirror; and this fact can be easily verified by looking closely at another person's eye, in which one will see a reduced image of himself. Fantz placed an infant chimpanzee in a crib which kept it from moving about and took pictures of its eyes from directly overhead while the animal had the choice of looking at two objects. If one image was in line with the pupil, it could be assumed that the chimpanzee was fixing its gaze on that object. By taking successive motion-picture frames, it was possible to get an objective measure of both the choice of objects and the time that the chimpanzee spent looking at them.

The results showed that at one month of age a chimpanzee preferred looking at a cross rather than a circle. This same method is readily adapted to human infants and can be given at almost any age when the child can be persuaded to lie or sit quietly. Fantz found that the time of visual fixation was very brief until the end of the neonatal period at approximately six weeks of age, when the time of attention to various objects went up quite rapidly.

This is also the time when infants begin to give the social smiling response, which in itself implies the development of the capacity of visual discrimination. This capacity is therefore developed long before the time when the standard visual-cliff test can be given, although something might be determined by placing a young baby on a movable platform over the visual cliff and noting when he showed distress.

Tactile Stimulation. Babies are highly responsive to touch, and there is much evidence that neglected babies or those given a minimum amount of physical care, as is sometimes the case in orphanages, develop less rapidly than others and sometimes actually regress in development. This problem was first approached from the viewpoint of the emotional climate provided by the mother, or "tender, loving care", but the evidence derived from other animals indicates that the presence or absence of physical stimulation is more important than the manner of giving it.

This "need for stimulation" has many aspects. In the first place, only a few of the more precocious mammals are capable of self-regulation at birth, either physiologically or behaviorally. For example, raising an immature animal like a puppy by hand turns out to be an extremely complicated process. Normally, a mother dog stays with her new-born puppies nearly twenty-four hours a day, and she does much more than simply lie passively and allow them to nurse. When she is away from the puppies, they will lie quietly in a pile, even if she is kept away for several hours, but as soon as she returns she starts nosing and licking them, stirring them up one after the other until they are all awake and moving. Stimulated by her touch and vigorous licking, they begin crawling around blindly until they make contact with a nipple and begin to nurse.

This kind of maternal care and stimulation is difficult to duplicate through human care. In raising a puppy by hand, we find that he must be stimulated in just the right way in order to produce appropriate behavior. A puppy does not readily take an ordinary nursing bottle. If held around the middle, he throws his head from side to side instead of nursing, and one has to hold him around the muzzle in order to get him to suck properly. If he is allowed to nurse only when he appears to be hungry and to stop feeding when he appears to be full, the result is a very skinny puppy. "Demand feeding" simply does not work well in this species.

Defecation and urination take place only when the genital and anal areas are stimulated with something resembling a mother's tongue, such as a warm, wet towel. In addition, new-born puppies cannot regulate their own temperatures, and those that are isolated have to be kept in a room at eighty-five or ninety degrees Fahrenheit. The young puppy is not a self-sufficient organism, and any attempt to rear him with an inanimate "model mother" which does not provide active tactile stimulation is bound to give very poor results.

Rats are born in an even more immature state than puppies. They are not only blind and deaf and limited in their motor capacities, but they are also born hairless. They cannot survive without the care and protection of the mother who builds them a warm nest, within which they normally pass their entire early life. A wild rat mother may sometimes move her young to a new nest if disturbed, and this occasionally happens with tame rats as well. However, in the usual laboratory situation the environment provides little stimulation other than that which a caretaker provides by adding food and water. The temperature is kept constant, and the room is usually quiet except for noises made by other rats. Consequently, the young rat lives in an unusually calm and constant physical environment. In this way the laboratory environment resembles that of a well-run hospital or orphanage.

Many of the early experiments with stimulating young rats consisted simply of picking them out of the nest one at a time, placing them in a separate cage, and then returning them. Treating them in this fashion not only stimulates the young rats directly but also causes the mothers to pay attention to them by nosing and rearranging them in the nest. This extra handling is comparable to the sort of experience which human infants might get in an orphanage if a nurse gave them extra care and attention. At any rate, the results are quite remarkable and, for the most part, are beneficial to the young rats. Denenberg (1967) and his colleagues at Purdue University have repeated these experiments in great detail and have analyzed the effects in many ways. In general, the handled rats grow up to be hardier adults. They grow faster, live longer, and stand physical stress such as lack of food better than animals which have been left undisturbed. Their behavior is affected in many other ways, but one of the basic effects is to make them calmer when they are placed in a strange large pen without a top (usually called an "open field"). In this situation, the previously handled rats defecate less, indicating that they are less emotionally disturbed by the strange situation.

Handling has its most pronounced effect during the neonatal period, which lasts until the rat is approximately ten days old, and is most effective during the first week of life. Since young rats are so immature at this time, these profound effects raise the problem of exactly how later behavior is affected.

To answer this question, Levine (1962) and his co-workers attempted first to find out what sort of stimulation the rats received from the handlings. Much to their surprise, they found that a large variety of physical stimuli would produce the same effect as gentle handling. Among other things, they tried electric shock and shaking in a mechanical shaker used for mixing chemicals. Schaefer (1967), who had done some of the original work on early stimulation, established cold as another source of stimulation. The temperature of young rats falls rapidly when they are taken from the nest. Schaefer showed that if he cooled them off without giving them extra tactile stimulation, by merely placing the whole cage including the mother rat and her offspring in a refrigerator, the young rats showed the same effect on later behavior. The Russian physiologist I. A. Arshavsky (1968) has suggested that the beneficial effects of moderate lowered temperature on growth result from increased heart and muscular activity as the homeostatic and stress mechanisms come into play.

All of these stimuli have one thing in common: ·They are physiologically stressful and therefore should produce increased activity of the adrenal glands. Such changes in adrenal activity are indeed found in young rats subjected to the above experiments, (Levine and Mullins, 1966) and early stimulation thus has the effect of activating this part of the general endocrine system. Since this system is still in an immature state in the newborn rat, its development can be modified. Levine concludes that laboratory rats are so protected in their early life in the nest that they do not receive sufficient stimulation to enable complete development of the endocrine system. This affects not only their physiology but their behavior at a later date.

These results again confirm the principle that stimulation is necessary for the development of basic behavioral capacities. In this case it is the organization of the endocrine system which is directly affected, with long-range effects on physical health and emotional development. Unlike deprivation of visual stimulation, whose effects are gradual and spread out over long periods, there is a definite critical period during which stressful stimulation will produce major effects upon the development of the endocrine system.

Do these results, which have been obtained almost entirely with rats, also apply to human beings? Babies are reared in a great variety of ways, all reflecting the fact that the human infant is completely incapable of moving itself from place to place and must be carried. Some tribes of American Indians developed the cradle board on which the baby was completely immobile while being carried. In other societies babies are constantly carried on the hips of their mothers or caretakers. In still others they are wrapped in swaddling clothes so tightly that they cannot move. In our own society styles change from time to time, from cradles to baby carriages and even to automobiles. One current solution is to keep the baby warmly clothed and able to move its arms and legs freely, but confined to a crib and watched by a baby sitter rather than being carried wherever the mother goes. It has even been suggested that the crib should be air conditioned and held at a constant temperature so that clothes would be unnecessary. This raises the question of whether such babies might not be understimulated, and indeed there are many reports that babies reared in orphanages or kept in hospitals and given a minimum of handling may become behaviorally depressed and even physically ill, in contrast to active and healthy children reared in families. Certainly, long-continued restriction of movement will lead to great motor retardation. (Dennis, 1960).

In general, the widely different methods of rearing babies do not seem to produce great differences in adult behavior. However, Landauer and Whiting (1964) surveyed a large sample of primitive societies where measurements of adult size are known, and have discovered that members of those societies in which some drastic treatment of new born infants is practiced, such as plunging them into cold water, or circumcision (or. scarification, or head moulding or the like), are on the average taller than members of societies which do not practice such drastic treatment. Of course, there are many other circumstances which might account for the results, and we should not quickly conclude that new-born babies should be treated roughly for their own good or dunked in icewater every morning to help them grow, even if our only criterion of human value was increased size. Incidentally, Landauer and Whiting point out that this function in our society may be filled by our practice of inoculation. The baby's experience of being stuck with a needle and his subsequent physiological reaction to a foreign protein may serve the same purpose as the more violent ceremonial methods of primitive societies. Therefore, the increase in average height observed in Western European societies since 1800 may be in part the result of the discovery of inoculation as well as the result of improved nutrition.

In any case, all the evidence indicates that tactile stimulation in early infancy is not only desirable but essential to normal development. Such stimulation is regularly provided in the course of the constant care and attention which a mother gives her child. Her treatment is ordinarily gentle, but no harm is likely to result from brief changes in temperature and occasional bumps. On the other hand, the baby does not need to be constantly stimulated and in early infancy normally spends most of its life resting and sleeping. In short, the evidence indicates that human development is designed to proceed normally under conditions in which considerable but not continual physical stimulation of many kinds takes place during waking hours, and that drastic reduction of this stimulation may impair development.

MOTOR CAPACITIES

There are tremendous individual differences in the rate of development of motor skills. In the sample of children studied by

Gesell (1940), babies might start to walk as early as eight and as late as eighteen months with a median of fifteen months of age. Presumably, much of this difference is caused by differences in heredity, although the effect of early experience cannot be excluded. Because the opportunities for motor learning vary a great deal between families, it is very difficult to get authentic information on the effects of early training and practice.

The effect of differential training on twins. Only one major experiment of this kind has ever been done. Myrtle McGraw (1939) obtained the cooperation of a mother of twin boys who were diagnosed as being identical and attempted an extensive experiment on their behavior, in which she gave one boy a great deal more practice than the other in various motor skills. She apparently produced major effects on the behavior of the two boys, but unfortunately it turned out that the twins were probably not identical, and the possibility was therefore present that the more practiced twin might have been more physically gifted in the first place. Nevertheless, the results lead to conclusions which appear to be reasonable.

To begin with, practice and encouragement had little effect on the development of the boys' capacity for adult locomotion. Both the twins walked at about the same time, and there was no indication that previous encouragement had any effect.

One of the unusual motor skills taught to the practiced twin was roller skating, and he learned to do this well between the ages of one year and fourteen months—almost as soon as he could walk. Actually, a young child with his short legs and low center of gravity can learn to keep his balance more easily than an older one.

Other kinds of motor skills were actually impaired by early training. The tutored baby was unable to master them and formed poor habits of coordination, with the result that the untutored twin actually did better at the same skills when he tried them at a later age with no advance training.

The final result of the roller skating was interesting in this regard. The practiced twin did not roller skate again until he was five or six years old. At this point the trained twin turned out to be actually more awkward than his brother because he had learned his early skills in connection with different body proportions, and these early habits interfered with his new learning. Many people have this experience at a much later age as a result of the adolescent spurt in growth. Here, learned habits for sitting down or going through doors are based on a much smaller physical size, so that the adolescent appears and feels awkward until he is able to readjust.

McGraw concluded that "there are critical periods when any given activity is most susceptible to modification through repetition of performance". The critical period in each case is the time following the age when the child is first capable of performing the act effectively. Johnny, the practiced twin, was first given training in tricycling at eleven months, and improved very little until nineteen months, when he improved rapidly, but not so rapidly as his twin who started at twenty-two months. Starting training either too early or too late is likely to produce inferior performance.

The complete development of muscular coordination is therefore dependent upon function, just as the complete development of muscle cells and the consequent maintenance of muscular tone are dependent upon exercise. Here we return again to the importance of function as a factor influencing development.

Effects of rearing animals in a simplified environment. Most of the experiments of this kind have studied the effects of a simplified environment upon problem solving rather than upon motor skill. However, the effects on motor behavior are quite obvious. Working at the Jackson Laboratory, Albert Pawlowski once reared a dog from birth in a small area with a floor space measuring approximately two by four feet. Never having had any other experience, the animal was not psychologically disturbed and appeared physically healthy. However, when finally released it was very awkward at running compared with puppies reared in larger spaces, and it moved in short hops rather than running freely.

In another instance, puppies were reared in a one-acre field. In contrast to those reared in large nursery rooms, these puppies appeared extremely skillful when brought into the same environment and dashed from one part of the room to another with great rapidity. Another litter of puppies was reared in a small room with a completely flat floor until they were five months old. At this point they were moved to an outside run in which the house was elevated a couple of feet above the ground. Ordinarily, dogs easily jump into such a house to sleep or to obtain food. In this case a broad ramp was added to the house in order to make it even easier for the inexperienced puppies to climb up to it. When placed inside the house, they all managed to climb or jump down to the ground again, but none of them got back up. Although their only food was placed in the house, none of the puppies managed to learn to climb up it for several days, after which they were removed to other quarters to protect their health.

On the other hand, some animals can learn motor skills even after maturity. Baron, Antonitis, and Schell (1962) reared young mice under a glass plate which prevented their climbing until they were four to five months of age, or well into maturity. Although when first given the opportunity to climb they did much less well than control animals, by another four months of practice the differences had largely disappeared.

Optimum periods of motor learning. From her experiments with Johnny and Jimmy, McGraw came to the conclusion that there is a critical period of development which determines the optimum time for the learning of any motor skill. For the most part, these optimum periods have not been scientifically established, and as a result, traditional times for teaching motor skills to babies and young children may depart considerably from the optimum except in individual cases. As McGraw suggests, the optimum period comes at the time when motor capacities have matured to the point where learning first comes quickly and easily. Since in some cases the development of the capacity is dependent upon practice itself, such an optimum period is difficult to establish and may differ from individual to individual. In the absence of concrete practical information, the best recommendation for an ideal physical environment that will encourage the maximum development of motor skills in young children is one which permits a great deal of freedom of movement. Obviously, a child confined to a playpen or even to a small apartment is not likely to develop skill in running. On the average, Negro babies in their first year develop their motor capacities more quickly than white children, but Pasamanick (1946) has pointed out that Negro mothers often allow their infants much more freedom of movement and contact with physical objects than do white mothers, who tend to keep their children in cribs and playpens as long as possible. The differences between white and Negro children are quite small compared with those between white babies reared in an orphanage and those reared by their parents or in foster homes. The orphanage babies lag far behind the rest, presumably because they are given less freedom of movement. Similarly, motor development of Negro babies in upper economic class homes lags behind that of babies in lower class homes, where they are given more freedom of movement (Williams and Scott, 1953).

It is also desirable to give a child contact with a variety of physical objects which can be manipulated or climbed. This encourages the development of general motor skills that can be applied later to the learning of more complicated tasks. The results at both ages are more satisfactory than those obtained by trying to teach complex physical skills directly at an early age. Most children are not able to perform activities requiring good coordination of the whole body much before the ages of 7 or 8, and introducing them too early to such activities only results in unskillful performance or failure.

EFFECTS ON THE DEVELOPMENT OF LEARNING CAPACITIES

Animal experiments.   Suspecting that his laboratory rats reared in small cages were showing the effects of living in an impoverished environment, D. O. Hebb (1947) of McGill University took some of them into his home and allowed them to be brought up as pets. This not only greatly increased their social contacts with people but also gave them a great variety of physical objects to explore and a much less limited area in which to live. When these rats were taken back into the laboratory as adults and tested in the Hebb-Williams maze, they did much better than controls reared in the usual cages.

From a scientific viewpoint, these home-reared rats grew up in a situation in which many variables were uncontrolled. Subsequent investigators have standardized the "enriched environment" for rats as a large laboratory cage containing a number of physical objects and playthings. Compared with the opportunities for exploration and manipulation afforded a wild rat or a tame one in a human household, this artificial "free environment" is greatly restricted, but it still produces large results when contrasted with rearing in barren laboratory cages.

Forgays and Read (1962) experimented with the effects of a three-week exposure to the free environment cage at different ages and found that early experience had no effect on performance in a standard Y-maze, which tests reactions to a fixed problem. However, rats raised in the free environment cage performed better than usual in the Hebb-Williams maze, which presents a series of problems in which animals choose the best of several alternate ways to a goal. The best scores were obtained by rats exposed to the free environment immediately after weaning at twenty-one days of age. Although the results from this experience were almost as good up to three months of age, they were considerably worse thereafter. The results on infant rats which lived in the large cage only until they were twenty-one days old were again not as good as those obtained directly after weaning, although these animals still did better than the controls, which had never had the experience at all. Thus there is an optimum period for the effect of a free environment shortly after weaning, as the same amount of time spent in this environment produces a less favorable result in both younger and older animals.

Some light is thrown on the above results by the experiments of Candland and Campbell (1962), who tested rats for their responses to the "open field" at various ages. Each rat was tested only once, and the amount of defecation and activity recorded. Exposure at eighteen to twenty-three days produced no effect on defecation, but after this the rate rose rapidly, especially between twenty-three and thirty days. It continued to rise more slowly until the rats were fifty-four days old, and then fell off gradually. The activity rate showed a similar curve, but the increase began sooner, occurring after eighteen days. These changes in emotional and investigative behavior coincide with the age during which the maximum effect is obtained by exposing an animal to a free-environment cage.

As Denenberg (1967) found in his experiments, the behavior of rats in an "open field" has two components, a fearful reaction and a tendency to investigate and explore the new situation, and the fact that these reactions develop at slightly different times supports this conclusion. Both of these components help explain the results of exposure to a complex free-environment cage. In the first place, there may well be a critical period for exploratory behavior in rat development around the time of weaning, when young rats are first sufficiently mature to leave the nest on their own. Practice in this early exploratory behavior should form a habit which would then carry over into later life.

This would not exclude the second possibility, that the time after weaning is a critical period for developing confidence in a familiar situation (and, conversely, fear of strange situations), with the result that the rat behaves confidently, and hence efficiently, only in those situations resembling its familiar early environment. Support for this hypothesis comes from the work of Campbell (1967) and his associates. Rats at this age forget learned fears more readily than do older animals and hence should be able to acquire confidence more easily in a new situation.

Still another line of evidence comes from the experiments of Krech and Rosenzweig (Bennett, *et al*, 1964), who found that placing rats in the free-environment cages resulted in an actual enlargement of the brain, especially in parts of the cerebral cortex. However, this effect can be produced equally well at any age following weaning and thus is not correlated with the differential effects on problem solving produced by enrichment experiments at certain ages. The phenomenon of cortical enlargement is another confirmation of the principle that stimulation promotes the development of nervous tissue, but in this case the stimulating effect is not limited to early development.

Critical periods of learning. The rat experiments with enriched environment indicate that there are critical periods during which the development of learning capacities can be easily enhanced. These periods seem to occur shortly after the time of weaning, when the infant animal has developed some independence and still has not developed strong fear reactions to strange objects. Such periods have not yet been identified in human development, but two obvious possibilities exist. One should occur after the child develops the capacity for walking and independent lomocotion and has also acquired a full set of teeth so that he can live on solid food. This period, which usually occurs around the age of two, is the first time when children have the basic capacities for a moderate degree of physical independence. We would expect a child to develop a tendency to explore and be curious about the world at this stage of development, and indeed there are many cases of children who wander away from home and become lost at this age. A second possibility is the period after seven or eight years of age, when the child first becomes physically independent in the sense of being able to run swiftly and learn other complex acts involving physical coordination. One would expect this to be the first age at which primitive children could leave their original social group and still survive, and that this would again be a time in which curiosity and investigatory behavior could be appropriately expressed.

In addition to these theoretical predictions, another critical period for learning obviously occurs in human beings: the age in which language can be learned easily and perfectly. Beginning at about the age of two, any normal child can learn any language, and many children easily learn two languages at this time. As a child grows older, learning a second tongue becomes increasingly difficult, and there are few people who have learned a foreign language in high school or later who can either speak it with a good accent or write it with facility unless they have expended long hours of tedious effort. This phenomenon, which involves both auditory stimulation and motor coordination, is one which deserves a great deal of study both from a practical and a theoretical viewpoint.

An interesting parallel is found in the development of certain songbirds which learn their songs by hearing adults sing. Thorpe (1965) reared chaffinches (one of the common English songbirds) in isolation starting at three or four days after hatching and found that such birds produce incomplete songs as adults. However, if an isolated male fledgling hears the song of an adult when he is two or three weeks old, he will reproduce the normal song a year later, even if he is kept in isolation in the meantime. Furthermore, adult birds do not modify their songs as a result of hearing other birds. Like people, chaffinches find it difficult to modify learned vocalizations as adults.

Enriching the early environment. McGraw's experiment with the twin boys indicated that practice and contacts with a variety of physical objects at critical periods will speed up and amplify the processes of development of motor skills. However, reliable indices of problem-solving abilities and intelligence cannot be obtained until children are much older, after they have had some formal school training or its equivalent. By that time all results indicate that children having a restricted environment, either at school or at home, do less well on intelligence tests than those reared in more favorable environments. Whether this result is related to very early infantile experience is difficult to determine. A comparison can be made between children attending nursery school and those who do not (Swift, 1964), but the nursery-school environment may or may not be more varied than that which the child already has at home. Nevertheless, we would expect that a child's intellectual development should be strongly affected by its opportunities to explore and become familiar with a complex physical environment and particularly in areas where the child can easily relate later learning tasks to his early experience.

It is obvious that such an effect could become a self-enhancing one in a competitive society such as ours. The more capable a child is, the more he becomes able to provide himself with an enriched environment which enhances his capability still more. Children raised in an enriched environment would thus become capable of providing comparable or better surroundings for their own offspring, while children raised in an impoverished environment would be less likely than others to develop sufficiently to improve it and would therefore tend to rear their own children in the same impoverished conditions. In an effort to break this vicious cycle, various "head-start" educational programs have been undertaken throughout the United States. These essentially consist of taking preschool children out of their impoverished homes for short periods and subjecting them to new experiences and especially to those experiences, objects, and people that they are likely to meet again in school. Here is an instance where research on animal behavior has led directly to an application to a basic human problem.

We shall not know what the payoff will be for many years and perhaps not until a new generation appears on the scene. Meanwhile, basic research on this problem should go forward both with human children and on other animals. We know less about the timing of the optimum period for a child's exposure to an enriched environment than we do for that of a young rat. It may be that the nursery school and kindergarten ages are already past the optimum period, and that the most effective time for laying the basis for the development of learning capacities is during the long period of preverbal learning that comes before the age of two years. We could better predict the outcome of providing an enriched environment if we understood the basic nature of the factors which produce differential results at different ages. Among the possibilities suggested by the animal experiments are the formation of negative learning sets, *i.e.,* under certain circumstances the animal learns not to learn. Such a result can be produced in many different ways, but one of the most important is simply the experience of failure. An animal that continually fails in a situation soon stops trying. Another way is the association of an unpleasant emotional response with an experience. This association can be a result of fright or pain felt during the learning experience or it may come about as a consequence of being placed in a strange situation or being exposed to strange animals. Such emotions could of course lead to failure and consequently to lack of motivation. Seen in this light, the head-start programs should at least have the effect of reducing some of these emotional factors.

Finally, there is the problem of social motivation. Almost all learning in the early school environment takes place within the social relationship developed between pupil and teacher. If the pupil's early environment has not prepared him to develop a reasonably close and pleasant relationship with his teacher, his motivation and consequently his learning capacities may suffer. All of these problems pose questions which can be at least partly answered by experiments with early experience on other animals.

EMOTIONAL ATTACHMENT TO PHYSICAL SURROUNDINGS

One of the well-established results of the above experiments is that rats become emotionally disturbed when placed in a strange environment. This phenomenon is so basic and so widespread in other animals that it deserves study for its own sake. Almost all animals become attached to a particular locality early in life and attempt to return to it if they are taken away. Even in the case of birds which migrate thousands of miles, the journey is always made between two definite localities.

The process of forming an emotional attachment to a particular set of physical surroundings may be called *primary localization*, indicating that it is quite similar to the process of primary socialization, or forming an attachment to the particular individuals in the social environment.

Beginning at about three weeks of age, a young puppy will begin to whine and yelp if it is left alone in its home pen. If placed alone in a strange place it will yelp two or three times as often as when alone in a familiar environment. Putting another puppy with it will slow the rate of vocalization well below that which it shows when isolated in its home pen but will never eliminate the reaction completely. Thus, very soon after its eyes open, the puppy becomes attached to a particular set of physical surroundings as well as to other animals (Scott and Bronson, 1964).

When human infants are taken from their mothers and placed in strange places, they begin to be emotionally disturbed soon after six weeks of age. At this time the rate of crying of infants brought into strange situations for physical and psychological examinations begins to increase (Bayley, 1932). Thus we have good evidence that human beings as well as other animals form emotional attachments to particular areas very early in life and feel emotionally disturbed if moved out of them. What effect do these attachments have on later behavior?

Obviously, people can move about from place to place as adults without serious emotional disturbance, and they also have the capacity to become attached to new places in later life. Perhaps the most that remains of an individual's early attachment is a feeling of safety and contentment when he returns to a familiar area. At any rate, many people who have led an active and wandering life eventually return to the scenes of their childhood.

We may also raise the question of what effect the emotion caused by an early change in locality has upon a child's later behavior. What an infant learns from such an experience should depend upon the circumstances. If he is taken out of his familiar environment long enough to become acutely distressed and then returned, he should learn that being in the area is pleasant and being elsewhere is unpleasant, and he should consequently become unusually attached to the familiar locality. Other possible consequences might be an association of strong emotional distress with the strange locality, with the result that the child would dislike it in the future. Whether the long-term effects are serious or not, it is obviously the best policy, from the viewpoints both of kindness and possible emotional damage, to make forced transitions from one place to another as pleasant as possible for young children.

SUMMARY

The most general principle which applies to early experience with the physical environment is that stimulation is necessary, both for the proper development of the nervous and neuroendocrine systems and for the development of behavioral capacities. The two senses with which most experimental work has been done are the visual and tactile senses. In the chimpanzee the ganglion cells of the retina are permanently damaged by prolonged absence of visual stimulation. Other species do not seem to be so drastically affected, although biochemical changes can be detected in the retina of a cat. In the case of the rat, where normal development in the wild species takes place in the dark, little or no damage results from lack of visual stimulation. Developmental dependency upon stimulation is therefore affected by differential heredity and is related to the kind of physical environment and stimulation to which any particular species has become adapted in the course of evolution.

Tactile stimulation is particularly important in the development of animals born in an immature state. Rats are less easily disturbed by strange situations as adults if they have been handled in infancy. This effect is not caused by tactile stimulation per se, but can also be produced by cold, electric shock, or any stimulus which activates the general stress reaction of the body. This involves the function of the adrenal glands, and the effect is to promote the development of this portion of the neuroendocrine system at a critical period in early development. There is some evidence that early stressful stimulation in human beings may have similar effects.

A second and subsidiary principle is that there are critical or optimum periods for stimulation which depend on the nature of the developmental processes concerned. Critical periods for the acquisition of certain motor skills occur at the times when the developing individual is first capable of performing them easily. There are also critical periods for certain kinds of learning experiences, particularly those resulting from contact with a complex environment that permits considerable freedom of action. Experience in such periods affects the performance of rats in certain problem-solving situations, and the same effect is probably also found in children. On the other hand, there appear to be no specific critical periods for the effects of visual stimulation upon the retina or for the effects of an enriched environment upon the growth of the cerebral cortex.

Where critical periods for learning exist, their effects are at least partially related to the phenomenon of developing an emotional attachment to particular physical surroundings. The result is that the young animal becomes relaxed and confident in a familiar place but excited and timid in a strange one. If the early environment is too narrowly restricted, the growing human or animal infant will find almost any other situation to be strange, will thus become timid or fearful in many environments, and so will perform less effectively.

Given the present state of our knowledge, the best physical environment in which to rear a child is one that gives him experience with a variety of physical objects which he can manipulate and contact freely with minimal restriction. This experience will give him an opportunity to develop basic motor skills which he can later apply to more specific learning situations. Giving the child more than one experience of this kind will make him feel familiar and confident within a variety of environments with which he may come into contact as an adult, but shifting him from one to another should be done in a way which avoids the acute emotional reactions produced by a sudden change into an entirely strange environment. The child should thus be given the opportunity to organize his behavior in relation to a known physical world, starting out from a well-known center and adding additional areas of familiarity in widening circles.

7 PRINCIPLES OF EARLY DEVELOPMENT

So far in this book we have approached the problems of early experience by attempting to examine systematically the various factors which influence behavior in early life. In this chapter we shall abandon this empirical viewpoint and attempt to establish some general theoretical principles.

THE PROCESS OF LEARNING

In earlier chapters we emphasized the fact that early learning is different from later learning. Just how different it is has never been completely established, but we do know that in both newborn children and puppies the capacity for learning is quite limited. Both kinds of infants make associations much more rapidly in connection with sucking than they do with painful stimulation, and their ability to learn is greatly limited by their undeveloped sensory and motor capacities. Basic questions still to be answered are the exact ways in which learning capacities change and whether or not the simple learning which goes on in the neonatal organism has persistent effects. We can, however, draw certain conclusions from what is known about the general nature of learning processes.

Habituation. When a young puppy first reaches the end of the transition period he appears to be highly sensitive to many changes in his environment. He gives a violent startle response to any loud noise, responding to slamming doors, barking dogs, and even to much milder noises. A few weeks later it takes an extremely loud and unusual sound to elicit a startle response, which is rarely seen thereafter. This process of ceasing to respond to stimuli that have no direct consequences for the animal is called *habituation.* Its nature is diagrammatically illustrated whenever a reflex is repeatedly stimulated. A young puppy will jump violently the first time it hears a loud noise. The second response is less extreme, and if the noise is made four or five times in rapid succession, the response may disappear entirely. After a suitable rest, the reflex can be obtained again. The exact physical nature of the process of habituation is not known, but in effect it is quite similar to accommodation of the sense organs. As will be shown below, the effect of habituation can be made permanent by associative learning.

From the viewpoint of early experience, two principles are important. First, *a young child or any other young mammal is a non-habituated animal and is much more responsive to environmental stimuli than it is in later life.* A child shows a fresh interest where an adult becomes bored and becomes hyperexcited in situations where an adult is calm and unresponsive. Second, *the kind of early experience which a child undergoes will determine the kinds of stimuli to which he becomes habituated.* Obviously, an adult cannot become habituated to all stimuli, and if he moves into a quite different environment in later life he may again show the sort of fresh responsiveness typical of children. This may in fact be a partial explanation for what anthropologists call "culture shock", the intense emotional reaction resulting from an attempt to move into a completely different social environment.

Problem solving. The general process of learning can be seen in almost diagrammatic form in a young animal like the dog. In one of our experiments (Scott and Fuller, 1965), we set up a maze problem for puppies, trying out different sorts of apparatus until we found one which worked reasonably well. This was a multiple T-maze with wire-mesh walls through which the puppies could see but which still presented a very confusing appearance from the inside. It consisted of six units, each of which had one blind alley, and the puppy had to find its way outside, where it would be given a food reward and put back with its litter mates. When first put in the maze, the puppies became very excited and moved around at random, going into many of the blind alleys and sometimes repeating mistakes over and over again. They eventually found their way out and on subsequent days began to improve, making fewer mistakes at each trial. A few of the puppies eventually discovered that they could go through the maze without mistakes if they systematically observed the next section in front of them, and these animals went slowly and carefully through the maze and made no errors. However, they soon abandoned this careful method and reduced their behavior to the simple habit of making alternate right and left turns, which of course resulted in their going into some of the blind alleys.

From this example we can see that the series of events involved in problem solving includes several subprocesses. The first is variation in behavior. Without this no improvement in performance would be possible. Much learning consists of such trial and error variation in behavior accompanied by a second subprocess, the selective elimination of the kind of behavior which does not lead to results. Third, some puppies appeared to discover a general solution of the problem, learning not simply the direct path for this particular maze but a general method for staying on a direct path in all similar mazes. As a fourth subprocess, all of the puppies reduced their behavior to a simple habit, as a result of which their behavior became more and more predictable.

From the nature of these processes we may conclude that *as a young animal learns, its behavior will become more and more reliable and consistent.* This expectation was confirmed in another experiment in which puppies were trained to stay on the platform of a scale while being weighed. At first their behavior was highly variable. They adopted all sorts of postures and were either very quiet or highly active. As this experience was repeated in weekly trials, each puppy tended to adopt one posture such as standing, and one form of activity, such as attempting to escape. Another pup might consistently sit and remain quiet on the scales. The results are shown in Figure 7.1.

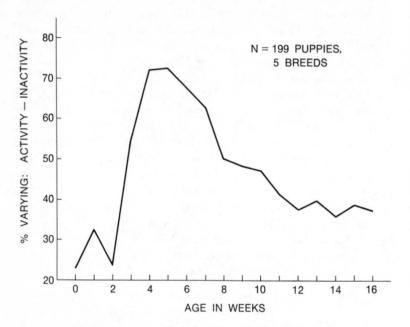

FIGURE 7.1 Development changes in variability of behavior in puppies. During the neonatal period the puppies tend to give only one reaction to being weighed, that of constant activity. As they grow older, they become highly variable, switching from activity to inactivity, and finally they become less variable, each puppy reacting consistently with either struggling or remaining quiet on the scales.

We can now draw several conclusions regarding the role of learning in early experience. The first of these is that as an individual grows older the variation in his behavior in any one situation will be reduced. Older people should be more consistent and reliable in their behavior than young children, and they generally are. Second, differences in early experience will result in differences in what an individual learns or does not learn. Of particular importance is the learning of general solutions to problems, as these facilitate later learning along certain lines rather than others.

A young organism may also learn a general method of not-learning. In the simplest example, a frightening experience or re-peated failure will lead an individual to avoid particular situations or to become passive in them. In one of our early maze experiments, the wall of the maze was not securely fastened, and when one of the puppies touched it, it fell down with a crash. This animal was so frightened that he would do nothing thereafter but crouch in the corner of the maze and refuse to move. His performance was conse-quently much poorer than those of his litter mates in the same test.

An even more drastic example of "learning not to learn" is the behavior of kennel dogs that have been given no training or experience other than good physical care. As older animals they are practically impossible to train by the methods which work easily and well on animals that have had some early learning experience. If taken out of the kennel at four to six months of age or older, they usually make very unsatisfactory house dogs, timid, difficult to house-break, and unresponsive to ordinary training. These animals act as if they had learned that anything which occurs outside their own pens has no significance for them, and when taken outside they simply wait until they are taken back.

Associational learning. Of all learning processes this one has been best documented and described. We still do not know the exact physiological basis of the process, but Pavlov and Skinner and their followers have worked out the nature of the phenomenon in great detail. The results can be described in terms of a number of general laws.

The first and most basic of these is the law of association. In Pavlov's experiments a dog would associate the sound of a buzzer with the subsequent appearance of meat and begin to salivate as soon as he heard the buzzer. Similarly, Skinner's rats associated the pressing of a bar with the appearance of a food pellet and, having pressed the bar, a trained rat would go over to the food-delivery tube and wait for a pellet. In general terms, we can say that if two events occur close together in time and are repeated later in the same order, an individual will act as if the first event produced the second. Once the first event occurs, he begins to prepare for the second.

As we have seen earlier, the ability to make rapid associations is quite limited at birth in both man and dog, and the complete story of the development of learning capacities is not yet known. However, we can conclude that *the effect of any particular early experience will depend upon the state of the learning capacities of the individual at that time.*

A second law of associational learning is that of reinforcement or strength of association. If two events at first occur together but later the second one does not follow the first, the response of the animal begins to weaken. In this way it can be demonstrated that *the strength of the association depends upon the number of repetitions or reinforcements.* This might also be called the law of habit strength. From it we can conclude that *a young animal early in life will have weaker habits than an older one.* The details of this phenomenon have only been worked out in connection with food rewards, but considerable evidence indicates that the strength of an association varies considerably depending on the kind of reinforcement and the nature of the response system (that is, whether skeletal or visceral muscles are used) as well as on the genetic nature of the individual involved.

All the evidence indicates that an association, once formed, produces an extremely long-lasting effect, perhaps extending over a lifetime. In Pavlov's dogs, the salivary response could be extinguished by lack of reinforcement, but with suitable periods of rest it would reappear again. In human beings, we all know of persons who at the age of eighty can clearly remember events which occurred in early childhood. The evidence justifies the conclusion that associations, once made, are permanent. However, this is at best a well-supported hypothesis, and we need to find out whether associational learning in early infancy has the same permanence as in later childhood. If learning really is permanent, it has very strong implications concerning the role of early experience. Assuming that something once learned can never be unlearned implies that if a person forms two conflicting associations, the first being based on a misleading experience, it will take about as long to make the second and correct association as strong as the first as it did to form the original erroneous one. In short, it should take about as long to break a habit as to form one in the first place. Again, we need more information on this point.

A corollary to the law of association is the law of negative association, or inhibition. Inaction as well as action can be associated with particular events. Not only will an individual learn to do nothing as a result of negative reinforcement such as fright or pain, but he can also learn to do nothing in a particular situation simply by doing nothing. *Early experience will thus determine certain patterns of inhibition or inaction that can have important consequences for later behavior.* It is perhaps no accident that young children and young animals tend to be highly active, for evolution would favor the survival of individuals who learned patterns of activity rather than of inactivity in early youth.

Finally, there is the law of discrimination and generalization. Once an association has been formed, an individual tends to give the same response in all similar situations, and as a result of experience he will learn to discriminate between those situations which are truly similar and those which are not. The nature of developmental changes in this capacity is not known, but we have some evidence that the power of generalization in young animals is quite limited. For example, we gave puppies a detour test in which they learned to go around a barrier fence (Scott and Fuller, 1965). If the length of the fence was extended, they showed some carry-over from what they had previously learned, but if the barrier was turned 180 degrees in the room, they reacted as if it were a completely new situation. If early learning tends to be specific (for the reason that very young organisms do not have the ability to generalize from special instances to whole classes of phenomena), it follows that *the effects of early experience tend to be specific rather than general.* Too severe toilet training, for example, should primarily affect eliminative behavior and should not affect sexual behavior unless the parent also punishes the latter.

We can conclude from these laws of associational learning that what an individual learns in early experience will affect what he learns or does not learn in the future. An association made with a particular event will at the very least make relearning difficult if the situation changes. Moreover, passive inhibition combined with generalization may cut off whole areas of later experience from the learning process, just as positive association combined with generalization can facilitate learning in wide areas. An individual can both learn-to-learn and learn-not-to-learn, and it is highly important for later existence that generally useful learning sets be formed.

Another implication of the laws of learning is that the results of early experience cannot be completely erased by later experience. They can be modified and even replaced to some extent, but relearning will take as long as original learning to form equally strong habits, and even in this case the individual is never the same as if he had formed only one unified habit.

We would expect that the process or processes of associational learning would interact with other processes. Association should result in the "freezing" of habituation, so that a stimulus which is repeated over and over again will eventually evoke no reaction even after rest. Thus the sounds which at first produce a startle reaction in a young puppy later produce no effect. We would further expect that the process of variation of behavior would act in opposition to associational learning and result in new solutions to problems even late in life. Long habit formation should render behavior more and more consistent, but the process of variation is always present, so that variation should never be reduced to zero. The habits established in early experience are not necessarily permanent.

Finally, we can conclude that the process of reinforcement or habit formation has major importance in determining future behavior, perhaps more so than the effect of a single traumatic experience or emotional shock. The important thing about such experiences is that they may determine the direction of a long process of habit formation rather than that they produce a tremendous effect in themselves. Indeed, this principle is now recognized in the treatment of individuals suffering from emotional shock, in that every attempt is made to treat them immediately and before the response can be set into a permanent habit pattern.

In this brief review of learning, we are obviously dealing with a group of related processes. Some of these work in opposition to each other, but all have the net effect of improving the individual's ability to adapt to an environment which may change from moment to moment and from generation to generation. It is also obvious that the behavior of an individual as he grows older becomes more and more organized. The processes of learning are organizational processes starting on very simple bases and proceeding to more complex ones.

The effectiveness of behavorial organization in any individual will depend on the nature of the organization achieved and its relevance to the world around him. An individual's behavior could be organized either for a stable world or for a rapidly changing one, but the results in either case would depend on outward circumstances. The importance of early experience is that *this is a time when organizational processes are proceeding most rapidly and hence can be modi-*

fied most readily. As organization becomes more and more fixed, it becomes more and more difficult to modify it without destroying it.

We can now consider other organizational processes that affect the development of behavior. These processes are on a different level of organization from that of learning, which acts primarily upon the behavior of the whole individual. The other processes chiefly co-ordinate the different parts of the body or even, in the case of gene action, act within the cell itself. Thus organization can take place on the physiological and even the molecular level.

GENETIC PROCESSES

The transmission of genetic factors. In transmitting the genes from one generation to another the chromosomes act in such a way as to produce variation. Only half the genes from each parent are passed along to any one offspring, and the half which is transmitted is selected purely at random. Thus the chromosomal mechanism is a reorganizing process, acting upon the gene pool, and creating new kinds of individuals and unique combinations of genes in each new generation.

Primary gene action. Genes are now known to be highly complex organic molecules, consisting of long chains of amino acids which can be arranged in an almost infinite variety of shapes. They act as organic catalysts, modifying chemical reactions. They do not act within themselves as a separate entity called "heredity," but act upon the surrounding environments, in most cases the collection of cellular chemicals which must themselves eventually come from the outside or be formed from outside material. Thus primary gene action organizes and changes the chemical raw materials which are available to it.

The primary effects of genes may be extremely remote from behavior itself, and the effects of genes upon behavior must usually be traced through an extremely complex series of reactions between cells, between genes, and between the organism and the environment. On the other hand, gene action can come very close to behavior in that genes may modify ongoing chemical processes at any time in life. Thus genes can modify the internal reactions of muscle cells and nerve cells and so produce a relatively direct effect on behavior.

Disorganizing genetic processes. The ultimate basis of varia-tion is mutation, or chemical changes in the genes themselves. One of the well-established facts of genetics is that the vast majority of mutations produce injurious effects. The greater the effect of the mutation, the more likely it is to produce a deleterious rather than a beneficial effect. The explanation is that in an extremely complex organism any change is more likely to be disruptive than beneficial. The general result is that major evolutionary changes in highly complex organisms occur very slowly.

PHYSIOLOGICAL PROCESSES

The genes themselves act primarily within living cells and make possible the processes which take place on higher levels of organization and contribute to eventual behavorial development. These higher-level processes are based on the activities of cells as wholes, and upon groups of cells organized into tissues and organs.

Differential growth. An embryo begins to take shape by growing at different rates. At first, the process of cell division simply results in an amorphous ball of cells, but soon certain areas begin to grow rapidly while others slow down. The rapidly growing areas tend to inhibit growth in other cells, and it is one of the interesting facts of embryology that the control of growth rests largely in the embryonic nervous system, just as the control and coordination of behavior later centers within this system. Thus intercellular control has passed from the genes to the cells and embryonic organs.

Differentiation. The cells not only grow at differential rates but become specialized in form and function. This process of histogenesis, or origin of specialized tissues, is incompatible with growth. Once specialized, cells lose much of their power of growth, and hence of reorganization. For example, in the central nervous system, the adult nerve cells cannot divide and increase in number although they can regenerate part of a nerve cell if it is cut off from the nucleus. Thus the processes of growth and differentiation tend to be self-limiting. Once completely organized, a higher animal can be reorganized only to a very limited extent.

Disorganizing factors of growth. There are no constant disorganizing processes connected with growth as there are with gene mutation, but organization can be disrupted by almost any major change in the external environment. Chemicals, drugs, temperature changes, and direct injuries can all disrupt the processes of growth and differentiation. Ordinarily, these effects are not specific, except that the part of the embryo which is growing most rapidly at the time is most likely to be injured. The central nervous system is the most rapidly growing part of the embryo during much of the first three months of human prenatal life, and this is the time when injury is most likely to occur. In addition, nervous tissue is very easily harmed by the loss of its oxygen supply at any time in life, and any prenatal or postnatal condition leading to anoxia may produce permanent damage.

In addition to these disorganizing external factors, there is in higher organisms an inherent collection of disorganizing processes, those connected with aging. These are not yet well understood, but seem to occur only partly as the result of the external environmental factors, and it is possible that the potentiality to develop these disorganizing factors exists in an organism from the very first.

Homeostatic processes. The process of growth organizes the form of an individual. As a result of this change in form it becomes possible for organization of function to take place. Early in development a set of processes begin that maintain a stable environment for the cells. The first of these is the circulation of the blood, which provides each cell with a supply of food and oxygen and carries away wastes as they accumulate. Circulation at first is completely self-regulating, but as the time goes on it begins to respond to bodily changes, the heart beating faster or slower and vessels expanding or contracting according to the needs of certain tissues. Such processes as these function according to the general principle of homeostasis, or maintenance of a stable internal environment. This principle, however, needs elaboration, because stability is not an end in itself. Rather, stability is maintained so that cells can continue to function well. As the cells become active, homeostatic processes are continually reacting and shifting in order to maintain stability. Furthermore, the successful function of the central nervous system requires a constant supply of oxygen under any conditions of activity. Homeostasis is strongly related to behavior because behavior itself calls for changes in physiological function, and homeostatic mechanisms are consequently subservient to behavior.

Homeostatic mechanisms are not organizing processes themselves but assist in maintaining organization. What are the organizing processes which set up homeostasis itself? Before birth most of the homeostatic processes are carried on by the body of the mother, but they must be ready to function after birth. Actually, homeostatic mechanisms function very inefficiently in many organisms born in an immature state. As we have seen, a new-born puppy cannot maintain its own body temperature at a constant level if it is separated from its mother and litter mates. As a result of experiments with rats on early stimulation, we now realize that at least some homeostatic mechanisms mature in response to stimulation in early development. This is another case of functional differentiation.

The regulation of homeostatic processes is achieved by neural and hormonal reactions, many of the latter being under the control of the nervous system also. Being under neural control, many physiological processes are subject to learning, as Pavlov first established with the salivary reflex. The effect of conditioning upon other internal organs has been little studied in relation to early experience, but what data we have suggests that the capacity for this sort of conditioning develops later than that for voluntary movement.

COMPARISON OF ORGANIZING FACTORS

It is interesting to compare the various processes of organization upon which behavior rests and to try to determine what they have in common. In the first place, they all must have a physiological basis. Even the process of learning, although it has never been completely understood, must rest upon the activity of the nerve cells. The current theories of brain function indicate that there is not only a long known circuitry of interaction between cells, based on the connections between fibre tracts within the brain and leading out into various parts of the body, but that the primary phenomenon of learning may be an intracellular process based on chemical changes, rather than one based on cell interaction. It is an extraordinary coincidence that the nerve cells appear to be rich in RNA, one of the complex chemicals concerned with primary gene action. It now appears possible that the same basic chemical mechanism is used for the transmittal and storage of information within the nervous system as for the transmittal of genetic information in primary gene action.

The different processes of behavioral organization all have common characteristics in that they are easier to disrupt than to improve and that, as time goes on, their reorganization becomes increasingly difficult. In both the processes of growth and in the processes of learning there are critical periods. In both of these the time at which organization can be most easily affected is that at which organization is proceeding most rapidly.

There are also certain differences between learning processes and growth processes. Although behavorial organization produced by learning tends to become more fixed as an organism grows older, it is possible to organize behavior in early life so that it can be more readily reorganized at a later date, for the blocks to behavioral reorganization are chiefly the formation of fixed and rigid habits and particularly of habits which exclude certain kinds of activity. Consequently, the formation of early habits directed toward flexibility and positive learning become enormously important.

Functional differentiation. Another general principle of organization which applies to both the process of learning and that of growth is functional differentiation. While an individual is still growing, function may alter the results of growth. For example, exercise will develop the circulatory system and muscles, and even bones will become strengthened and reinforced according to the strains put upon them. Similarly, the differentiation of behavior in relation to different environmental situations may be considered a lifelong process of functional differentiation. Stated in more specific terms, function modifies differentiation and the kind of function therefore influences the nature of organization. One of the principal effects of early experience is that it determines the nature of differentiation, and an obvious corollary is that the most desirable kind of early experience should be that which permits a maximum amount of differentiation of behavior. All of our current experimental evidence indicates that this kind of early experience is provided by contact with an "enriched" environment, i.e., one in which an individual is given contact with a large variety of physical objects and social companions.

THE DEVELOPMENT AND ORGANIZATION OF MOTIVATION

The older approach to the problem of motivation assumed a biological need which could be satisfied by means of behavior. For example, the tissues within the body, because of metabolic processes, soon use up the available nutritive elements. This sets in motion a chain of physiological reactions resulting in hunger contractions in the stomach that can be relieved by eating. However, this sequence should not be taken as a universal model for all motivation. The physiological mechanisms underlying other systems of behavior are known to be quite different and not necessarily dependent upon tissue needs.

We may conclude that motivation has multiple physiological sources, both from without and within the different behavorial systems. When we try to describe the development of these internal motivational mechanisms, we realize how ignorant we still are regarding the fundamental facts of development, particularly in human beings. At present, we have no good developmental studies of any major physiological processes, not even those found in nutrition, and in most cases we can only infer from external behavior what is actually going on within the organism.

In the neonatal stage, human infants appear to have already developed some sort of hunger mechanism as the motivational basis of ingestive behavior. They also react to cold and heat and so possess some of the physiological mechanisms associated with shelter- and comfort-seeking behavior. Whether or not they have internal fright mechanisms developed is still a matter of conjecture, and the only direct evidence comes from such reflex reactions as the startle response to sudden noises. The apparent anger or fright responses manifested in crying may be only a reaction to discomfort. Even if these mechanisms are present, we do not know how well they are developed compared with those in an older child or an adult.

In the period of socialization, beginning at approximately two months of age, the first motivational mechanism connected with allelomimetic behavior appears, as evidenced by the crying reaction to being left in strange situations. As visual capacities improve, babies begin to inspect their environment with increasing attention, indicating that motivation connected with investigatory behavior is present.

In the transition period, investigatory behavior becomes much more prominent, as a child is able to move around and actively explore the space around him. Only after the end of this period do babies begin to be responsive to bladder and bowel training, indicating that a motivational basis for eliminative training (in the sense of behavior other than internal physiological reactions) has developed.

It is difficult to find the exact point at which some indications of sexual behavior begin to appear, but judging from results with puppies and other animals, we can say that immature patterns of sexual behavior begin to appear as soon as general motor abilities are developed. Definite patterns of agonistic behavior begin to appear about the same time. Finally, care-giving behavior appears quite late in development.

Unsatisfactory as this information is, it indicates that the physiological sources of motivation develop at different rates and thus support Freud's general notion of stages of emotional development. We particularly need more observational and physiological information on these points, but since human infants are so inaccessible in the early stages, most of these facts will probably have to be derived indirectly from experiments with other animals.

We can summarize this information as follows:

1. There are multiple sources of motivation associated with different behavioral systems.
2. Each of these sources has a different physiological basis and special characteristics.
3. These sources develop at different rates.
4. Each of them can be modified by learning.

These facts lead to certain practical conclusions. The frustration or satiation of any particular source of motivation must have different effects at different ages. Until we know more about physiological development we will be unable to predict these effects exactly, but many of the motivational mechanisms appear to be much weaker in very early development and hence frustration should not produce immediate drastic effects. On the other hand, because inhibitory training should be relatively easy to accomplish while a motivational system is undeveloped, the persistence of early negative training might well lead to drastic consequences later, when the motivational mechanism is fully developed.

CONCLUSION

The nature of organizational processes. It is obvious that there are not only many different kinds of organizational processes going on in development but that each of these general classes includes many distinct and separate processes. These do not proceed at the same rates or at the same times, and this may be true even of certain closely related processes. For example, the physical maturation of the eye and ear in puppies occurs at different times in development in different breeds. Thus each of these developmental processes may be accelerated or slowed down by genetic factors without affecting the other and without producing appreciable affects on general development.

We can therefore state a general principle of *independence of organizational processes*. It follows that each process must be studied separately in order to determine the time and course of its development. When this is done we shall be in a position to describe a general plan of development in terms of probability, realizing that no one process will provide a developmental index for all the others. The important point here is that there is considerable flexibility in the development of organizational processes and that the course of one process cannot be predicted by knowing that of another.

The second general principle is that *organizational processes tend to be self-limiting*. As soon as organization is far advanced it becomes difficult to replace it or modify it, and the organism becomes incapable of starting again from the beginning. This effect is obviously true of growth processes in the higher animals, whose powers of regeneration in adult life are limited almost entirely to the healing of wounds.

Learning processes are somewhat more flexible in that it is possible to have learning organized in such a way as to facilitate additional learning. Nevertheless, anything which is learned tends to limit the nature of future learning. The self limiting nature of organizational processes results in the general principle that *organization of any kind tends to become stable*. Any change is more likely to upset than to benefit the system, and in most cases it is easier to institute an entirely new organizational process than to modify an old one. In a broad sense, this is what happens as each new generation replaces the old one.

Critical periods.   Against this background of general principles and understanding of organizational processes it is possible to establish a general theory of critical periods as well as to describe such periods as important objective phenomena. Organization can be modified most drastically and effectively at the time when it is proceeding most rapidly. *A critical period is therefore a period in which a given organizational process is proceeding most rapidly.* If a process proceeds at a constant rate throughout life, there can be no critical period. Or if a process proceeds at a uniform rate and comes to a stop, the entire time in which it takes place will be a critical period. The evidence concerning such processes indicates that neither of these possibilities is true in most cases but that a process may begin, proceed at a slow rate for a time, then become much more rapid, and finally be reduced to a slower rate again. This general pattern certainly applies to the process of learning and also to the process of developing social attachments. In studying developmental processes it therefore becomes necessary to determine their rates at different times in development. This will give us a parametric description from which it will be possible to make accurate predictions of the degree to which modification is possible. The designation of a critical period can then be derived directly and objectively from rate changes in an organizational process.

As the measurement of critical periods in processes of organization becomes more definite, the practical applications will become more precise. The knowledge of critical periods is a tremendously powerful tool in preventive mental hygiene, defined here as the prevention of maladaptive organization of behavior.

The psychodynamic approach to development. Considered from the above viewpoint, the dynamic approach to behavior used by Freud and his followers is an attempt to study organizational processes of behavior and behavioral development. The psychoanalytic method itself is an attempt to help a patient to reorganize his behavior on the assumption that his problems are caused by faulty organization. In keeping with the general principle that organization tends to be stable, the process of psychoanalysis usually takes a long time—frequently a matter of years—and even then it is not always successful. Further, the method is obviously limited to those cases in which the problems actually do rest on faulty internal organization and not on external circumstances.

The general principles of organizational development support the idea of periods of development characterized by certain processes. The oral, anal, and phallic periods of development are examples of periods in which organizational processes related to eating, elimination, and sexual behavior are taking place. These concepts now need to be re-examined and objective data obtained concerning them, keeping in mind that these processes may overlap in time and that many other important processes of behavorial organization may be going on as well.

The effects of early stimulation. Considering this phenomenon from the viewpoint of organizational processes, it is obvious that early stimulation can affect several different processes, and this may account for some of the confusion which exists in this field. In the first place, sensory stimulation appears to be necessary for the bio-local differentiation of the retina in certain species of animals. This is of course a special case of functional differentiation. Second, among mammals born in an immature state, an enormous change in the degree of stimulation takes place as soon as the infant emerges from the protection of the mother's homeostatic mechanisms. Many of the biological growth processes are not complete, and present evidence indicates that the development of hormonal mechanisms can be permanently modified by stimulation at this time. Finally, such an immature organism is not a complete self-regulating system and may require social stimulation in order to develop properly. It will certainly require a great deal of care and protection merely in order to survive.

The importance of early experience. We can now begin to understand why early experience has important effects. First, many important organizing processes proceed at their maximum rate early in life. Second, many organizational processes are self-limiting, and the nature of these limits is determined under the influence of early experience.

On the other hand, all early experiences are not necessarily important. If no organizing process is going on at the time, there will be nothing to affect. For example, in a young puppy the process of learning through visual discrimination does not begin until the eyes are open, and the most horrendous sights during the first two weeks of life will have no result. Further, if a process is going on over a long period of time, a single experience may have no important effect unless it in some way determines or limits the direction of future organization. This premise casts doubt on the importance of unique traumatic emotional experiences, unless such experiences have the effect of blocking further development of an organizational process. The kind of traumatic experience which is more likely to produce drastic effects is a long-continued one, as when a parent mistreats a child over a period of months or years.

These considerations bring up the question of whether early experience absolutely and finally determines later behavior. If it does, parents and teachers must bear a tremendous burden of responsibility for the next generation, as they have the power in a large measure to determine what a child's early experience may be. Fortunately there are several modifying circumstances. In the first place, young organisms are adaptable and flexible. Evolution has long proceeded in the direction of individuals who can adapt themselves to many different circumstances. The young organism is surprisingly tough and survives a great variety of parental behavior. In the second place, many organizational processes are buffered against outside events, and they tend to proceed unharmed or largely unaffected despite variation in the environment. For example, most children learn to talk by listening and talking with others, regardless of whether their parents consciously teach them. Finally, it is difficult to produce a direct one-to-one effect on an organizational process. It can be modified, but the effect usually is an adaptive reaction to external stimulation which may take a variety of forms.

The responsibility of a parent is therefore not to determine the exact course of development of a child's behavior, which is impossible, but rather to provide the circumstances under which it can develop most favorably. At the outset, a prospective parent who carries a known hereditary disease can avoid passing along his undesirable heredity by not having children. Having decided to have children, normal parents can help provide a favorable early environment for their future offspring, starting with the prenatal environment and extending their efforts to the early postnatal years.

All our present information indicates that the best environment at one stage in development is not necessarily the best at another. The benefits of a rich and varied environment are manifold when a child begins to learn about his physical environment, but a complex environment of books, pictures and museums obviously has little meaning to a child who is only six months old. The most favorable environment depends on the age of the child and his own particular rate of development. One of the most important practical rules is to permit a child a reasonable latitude of development by allowing him to organize his behavior himself rather than attempting to force it upon him. The most damaging effects of early experience come from too great restriction, whether of diet or social behavior. In the most general terms, the responsibility of a parent or teacher is to do what he can to provide the most favorable environment for the organization of behavior, but realizing that while his role is at first a central one, responsibility will ultimately develop in the child himself.

What can we accomplish with our knowledge of early experience? For a laboratory rat we can prescribe an enriched physical environment which will enhance his ability to perform on certain intelligence tests and a regime of infantile stimulation that will make him a hardier and more emotionally stable adult. For a rhesus money we can provide the opportunity for social play during the first six months of life that will ensure the development of normal sexual behavior in both sexes and proper patterns of infant care in the females. For the dog we can give a prescription for the development of a well-balanced animal with satisfactory social relationship with both dogs and people, simply by recommending that he be taken from the litter between six and eight weeks of age and then adopted into human society.

Making due allowances for human biological and cultural peculiarities, we ought to be able to make the same sorts of concrete recommendations for human upbringing, and indeed some application of the findings from basic research in early experience is being made in the "head-start" programs for children who are culturally deprived and in the treatment of young children who are separated from their families. Obviously the chief results of such research will be positive rather than therapeutic, and as new discoveries and better applications of them are made in the future, we should soon have the basis for a true science of preventive mental hygiene.

In the course of this book we have by implication presented the story of a slow revolution in developmental thinking: the replacement of static and anatomical concepts with concepts of ongoing processes. The complete implications of this scientific revolution are still to be worked out, but one of its consequences is to re-emphasize the importance of early experience.

REFERENCES

These references are arranged by chapters in two groups: general articles and reviews, followed by special references to experiments described in the text. Where information from an article or book is used in several chapters, it is listed only once in the first relevant chapter.

CHAPTER 1: Animal Infancy and the Evolution of Behavioral Development

CRUIKSHANK, R. M. Animal infancy. In Carmichael L. (Ed.), *Manual of child psychology*. New York: Wiley, 1954. Pp. 186–214. Review of older literature.

DE VORE, I. (Ed.) *Primate behavior*. New York: Holt, Rinehart and Winston, 1965. Excellent general survey of primate behavior.

LORENZ, K. Der Kumpan in der Umwelt des Vogels. *Journal für Ornithologie*, 1935, *83*, 137–213, 289–413. Lorenz' original studies on the phenomenon of imprinting in various species of birds.

STEVENSON, H. W., HESS, E. H., and RHEINGOLD, H. L. (Eds.) *Early behavior: Comparative and developmental approaches*. New York: Wiley, 1967. Chapters by various authors on special aspects of early development of behavior in human infants, chimpanzees, monkeys, cats, rats, squirrels, and altricial birds.

WALK, R. D. The study of visual depth and distance perception in animals. In D. S. Lehrman, R. A. Hinde, and E. Shaw (Eds.), *Advances in the study of behavior*, Vol. I. New York: Academic Press, 1965. Pp. 99–154. Review of methods of studying the development of visual perception.

Behavioral Development of Particular Species

BOLLES, R. C., and WOODS, P. J. The ontogeny of behavior in the albino rat. *Animal Behaviour*, 1964, *12*, 427–441. Excellent modern study of rat development.

COLLIAS, N. E. The development of social behavior in birds. *Auk,* 1952, *69,* 127–159. Early behavior in the domestic chicken compared with that of other birds.

DE VORE, I. Mother-infant relations in free-ranging baboons. In H. L. Rheingold (Ed.), *Maternal behavior in mammals.* New York: Wiley, 1963. Pp. 305–335. Behavioral development in baboons.

GUHL, A. M. The development of social organization in the domestic chick. *Animal Behavior,* 1958; *6,* 92-111. Effects of sex hormones on the development of agonistic behavior and dominance in the domestic chick.

HARLOW, H. F., and HARLOW, M. K. The affectional systems. In A. M. Schrier, H. F. Harlow, and F. Stollnitz (Eds.), *Behavior of non-human primates.* New York: Academic Press, 1965. Pp. 287–334. Behavioral development in the rhesus monkey.

JAY, P. Mother-infant relations in langurs. In H. L. Rheingold (Ed.), *Maternal behavior in mammals.* New York: Wiley, 1963. Pp. 282–304. One of the best general studies of infancy in primates.

KING, J. A. Development and behavioral evolution in *Peromyscus.* In W. E. Blair (Ed.), *Vertebrate speciation.* Austin: University of Texas Press, 1961. Pp. 122–147. Development of behavior in the deer mouse.

MASON, W. A. The social development of monkeys and apes. In I. DeVore (Ed.), *Primate behavior.* New York: Holt, Rinehart and Winston, 1965. Pp. 514–543. Behavioral development of the chimpanzee.

NICE, M. M. Studies in the life history of the song sparrow. *Transactions of the Linnaean Society of New York,* 1943 6, 1–328. (Reprinted. New York: Dover, 1964.) A classical study of bird behavior.

ROSENBLATT, J. S., and SCHNEIRLA, T. C. The behaviour of cats. In E. S. E. Hafez (Ed.), *The behaviour of domestic animals.* London: Balliére, Tindall, and Cox, 1962. Pp. 453–488.

SCOTT, J. P. Social behavior, organization, and leadership in a small flock of domestic sheep. *Comparative Psychology Monographs,* 1945, *18(4),* 1–29. Development of behavior in a herd animal.

SCOTT, J. P., and FULLER, J. L. *Genetics and the social behavior of the dog.* Chicago: University of Chicago Press, 1965. Detailed observational and experimental studies of behavioral development in the dog.

WILLIAMS, E., and SCOTT, J. P. The development of social behavior patterns in the mouse, in relation to natural periods. *Behaviour,* 1953, *6,* 35–64. Systematic study of behavioral development in the mouse.

CHAPTER 2: Periods and Processes of Early Human Development

AMBROSE, J. A. The development of the smiling response in early infancy. In B. M. Foss (Ed.)., *Determinants of infant behavior.* New York: Wiley,

1961. Pp. 179–195. Quantitative study of smiling in home-reared as well as orphanage infants.

EISENBERG, R. B., GRIFFIN, E. J., COURSIN, D. B., and HUNTER, M. A. Auditory behavior in the human neonate: a preliminary report. *Journal of Speech and Hearing Research*, 1964, 7, 245–269. Recent work on the development of auditory capacities.

FANTZ, R. L. Visual perception from birth as shown by pattern selectivity. *Annals of the New York Academy of Sciences*, 1965, *118*, 793-814. Excellent study of development of visual capacities.

_____. Visual perception and experience in early infancy: A look at the hidden side of behavior development. In H. W. Stevenson, E. H. Hess, and H. L. Rheingold (Eds.), *Early behavior: Comparative and developmental approaches*. New York: Wiley, 1967. Pp. 181–224. Additional experiments on the development of visual perception in human infants.

FREEDMAN, D. An ethological approach to the genetical study of human behavior. In S. G. Vandenberg (Ed.), *Methods and goals in human behavior genetics*. New York: Academic Press, 1965. Pp. 141–162. Effects of heredity on the development of smiling.

GEWIRTZ, J. L. The course of infant smiling in four child-rearing environments in Israel. In B. M. Foss (Ed.), *Determinants of Infant Behavior*. New York: Wiley, 1965. Effects of cultural differences on smiling.

LIPSITT, L. P. Learning processes of human newborns. *Merrill-Palmer Quarterly of Behavior and Development*, 1966, *12*, 45–71. Development of learning capacities.

_____. Learning in the human infant. In H. W. Stevenson, E. H. Hess, and H. L. Rheingold (Eds.), *Early behavior: Comparative and developmental approaches*. New York: Wiley, 1967. Pp. 225–247. Studies of habituation and conditioning in the newborn.

PAPOUSEK, H. Experimental studies in appetitional behavior in human newborns and infants. In H. W. Stevenson, E. H. Hess, and H. L. Rheingold (Eds.), *Early behavior: Comparative and developmental approaches*. New York: Wiley, 1967. Pp. 249–277. One of the best recent studies on developmental changes in learning capacities in human infants.

PRECHTL, H. F. R. Problems of behavioral studies in the new born infant. In D. S. Lehrmann, R. A. Hinde, and E. Shaw (Eds.), *Advances in the study of behavior*. Vol. 1. New York: Academic Press, 1965. Pp. 75–98. Recent studies on the development of motor capacities.

SCHAFFER, H. R. Objective observations of personality development in early infancy. *British Journal of Medical Psychology*, 1958, *31*, 174–183. Age changes in emotional reactions to separation from relatives.

SCOTT, J. P. The process of primary socialization in canine and human infants. *Monograph, Society for Research in Child Development*, 1963, 28,

1–47. Review of evidence for the existence of periods of development in the human infant.

SPITZ, R. A., and WOLF, K. M. The smiling response: A contribution to the ontogenesis of social relations. *Genetic Psychology Monographs*, 1946, 34, 57–125. The classical study of the development of social smiling.

CHAPTER 3: The Prenatal Development of Behavior

ANDERSON, V. E. Genetics in mental retardation. In H. A. Stevens and R. Heber (Eds.), *Mental retardation*. Chicago: University of Chicago Press, 1964. Pp. 348–394. Review of genetic factors affecting human intelligence.

MC KUSICK, V. A. *Human genetics*. Englewood Cliffs, N. J.: Prentice-Hall, 1964. Defects produced by hereditary factors.

REED, S. C. *Counseling in medical genetics*. Philadelphia: W. B. Saunders, 1963. Practical human problems resulting from genetically produced defects.

YOUNG, W. C., GOY, R. W., and PHOENIX, C. H., Hormones and sexual behavior. *Science*, 1964, 143, 212–218. Prenatal effects of the sex hormones.

Studies on Special Topics

DE FRIES, J. C. Prenatal maternal stress in mice: Differential effects on behavior. *Journal of Heredity*, 1964, 55, 289–295. The effect of prenatal stress depends upon the heredity of both mother and offspring.

GRAHN, D., and KRATCHMAN, J. Variation in neonatal death rate and birth rate in the United States, and possible relations to environmental radiation, geology, and altitude. *American Journal of Human Genetics*, 1963, 15, 329–352. High altitudes tend to cause premature births and greater neonatal mortality.

HAMMOND, J. Growth in size and body proportions in farm animals. In M. X. Zarrow (Ed.), *Growth in living systems*. New York: Basic Books, 1961. Pp. 321–334. Effects of maternal body size on prenatal growth.

MONGE, C. *Acclimatization in the Andes*. Baltimore: Johns Hopkins Press, 1948. Fascinating historical account of the effects of high altitude on reproduction and mortality.

PASAMANICK, B., and KNOBLOCH, M. Epidemiologic studies on the complications of pregnancy and the birth process. In G. Caplan (Ed.), *Prevention of mental disorders in children*. New York: Basic Books, 1961. Pp. 74–94. Studies of the effect of the environment on maternal health and resulting behavioral defects of children.

SONTAG, L. W. Differences in modifiability of fetal behavior and physiology. *Psychosomatic Medicine*, 1944, 6, 151–154. Studies on human behavior before birth.

THOMPSON, W. R., WATSON, J., and CHARLESWORTH, W. R. The effects of prenatal stress on offspring behavior in rats. *Psychological Monographs No. 557*, 1962, 1–26. The effects of maternal emotional states on the behavior of young rats.

CHAPTER 4: Critical Periods of Social Development

ALTUS, W. D. Birth order and its sequelae. *Science*, 1966, *151*, 44–49. General review of birth order in relation to superior performance.

BOWLBY, J. *Maternal Care and Mental Health*. Geneva: World Health Organization, 1951. Review of effects of disrupting maternal care.

GRAY, P. H. Theory and evidence of imprinting in human infants. *Journal of Psychology*, 1958, *46*, 155–156. Review of the evidence concerning the effects of adoption at different ages.

HESS, E. H. Imprinting and the critical period concept. In E. L. Bliss (Ed.), *Roots of behavior*. New York: Harper, 1962. Pp. 254–263. The primary socialization process in the domestic chick.

LORENZ, K. *Evolution and modification of behavior*. Chicago: University of Chicago Press, 1965. Contains a chapter on the technique of deprivation experiments.

SCHAFFER, H. R., and EMERSON, P. E. Development of social attachments in infancy. *Monograph, Society for Research in Child Development*, 1964, *29(3)*, 1–77. Observations on time and intensity of early social attachments.

SCOTT, J. P. Critical periods in behavioral development. *Science*, 1962, *138*, 949–958. General review of facts and theory relating to critical periods.

_____. The process of primary socialization in the dog. In G. Newton and S. Levine (Eds.), *Early experience and behavior*. Springfield, Ill.: Thomas, 1967. Summarizes experiments with this process in the dog.

SEARS, R. R., MACCOBY, E. E., and LEVIN, H. *Patterns of child rearing*. Evanston, Ill.: Row, Peterson and Co. 1957. Contains a chapter on child training in relation to ordinal position.

SLUCKIN, W. *Imprinting and early learning*. Chicago: Aldine, 1965. A concise review of the topic.

YARROW, L. J. Separation from parents during early childhood. In M. L. Hoffman and L. W. Hoffman (Eds.), *Review of child development research*. New York: Russell Sage Foundation, 1964. Pp. 89–136. Good critical review of the literature on this topic.

Special Topics

BOWLBY, J. Separation anxiety. *International Journal of Psychoanalysis*, 1960, *41*, 1–25. Summary of observations of infants' emotional reactions to separation from their mothers.

FREEDMAN, D. G., KING, J. A., and ELLIOTT, O. Critical period in the social development of dogs. *Science*, 1961, *133*, 1016–1017. The best experimental study of the critical period for primary socialization in this species.

FULLER, J. L., and CLARK, L. D. Genetic and treatment factors modifying the post-isolation syndrome in dogs. *Journal of Comparative and Physiological Psychology*, 1966a, *61*, 251–257. Some dog breeds are more severely affected by isolation than others; results of attempted therapy.

FULLER, J. L., and CLARK, L. D. Effects of rearing with specific stimuli upon post-isolation syndrome in dogs. *Journal of Comparative and Physiological Psychology*, 1966b, *61*, 258–263. Visual isolation has more severe effects than restriction of space alone.

HERSHER, L., RICHMOND, J. B., and MOORE, U. A. Maternal behavior in sheep and goats. In H. L. Rheingold (Ed.), *Maternal behavior in mammals*. New York: Wiley, 1963. Pp. 203–232. The herd animals rapidly form an exclusive bond with their young, as well as the young becoming attached to their mothers.

KLINGHAMMER, E. Factors influencing choice of mate in altricial birds. In H. W. Stevenson, E. H. Hess, and H. L. Rheingold (Eds.), *Early behavior: Comparative and developmental approaches*. New York: Wiley, 1967. Pp. 5–42. Experiments with imprinting in ring-doves and mourning doves, with a review of work on other altricial species.

KOCH, H. L. The relation of certain family constellation characteristics and the attitudes of children toward adults. *Child Development*, 1955, *26*, 13–40. This article and the three that follow contain some of the main results of Koch's studies on the effects of ordinal position on Chicago school children.

――――. Some emotional attitudes of the young child in relation to characteristics of his siblings. *Child Development*, 1956a, *27*, 393–426.

――――. Children's work attitudes and sibling characteristics. *Child Development*, 1956b, *27*, 289–310.

――――. Sissiness and tomboyishness in relation to sibling characteristics. *Journal of Genetic Psychology*, 1956c, *88*, 231–244.

KRUIJT, J. P. *Ontogeny of social behavior in Burmese red jungle fowl.* Leiden: Brill, 1964. Descriptive and experimental studies of behavioral development in the wild ancestor of the domestic chicken.

ROSENBERG, B. G., and SUTTON-SMITH, B. Ordinal position and sex role identification. *Genetic Psychology Monographs*, 1964, *70*, 297–328. Family rank chiefly affected feelings of anxiety in this study of Ohio school children.

SCHACHTER, S. *The psychology of affiliation.* Stanford: Stanford University Press, 1959. Experiments with older and younger sisters.

CHAPTER 5:   Effects of Early Experience on Social Behavior

BRACKBILL, Y. *Research in infant behavior: A cross-indexed bibliography.* Baltimore: Williams & Wilkins, 1964. Good bibliographic reference for human development.

CALDWELL, B. M. The effects of infant care. In M. L. Hoffman and L. W. Hoffman (Eds.), *Review of child development research*, Vol. 1. New York: Russell Sage Foundation, 1964. Pp. 9–87. Excellent critical review of research on differential methods of caring for human infants.

SCOTT, J. P. *Aggression.* Chicago: University of Chicago Press, 1958. General reference on the causes and control of fighting in man and other animals.

Special Topics

BEACH, F. A. Mating behavior of male dogs after restricted social contact in puppyhood. *American Zoologist*, 1965, *5*, 687. Abstract describing experiments with effects of isolation on later sexual behavior.

BRACKBILL, Y. E. Extinction of the smiling response of infants as a function of reinforcement schedule. *Child Development*, 1958, *29*, 115–124. Experiment on modifying the frequency of smiling through learning.

BRAZELTON, T. B. A child-oriented approach to toilet-training. *Pediatrics*, 1962, *29*, 121-128. Results of beginning toilet training at ages when capacity for continence should already be developed.

ELLIOT, O., and KING, J. A. The effect of early food deprivation upon later consummatory behavior in puppies. *Psychological Reports*, 1960, *6*, 391-400.

GEWIRTZ, J. L. The course of smiling by groups of Israeli infants in the first eighteen months of life. *Scripta Hierosolymitana*, 1965, *14*, 9–58. A comparative study of the development of smiling in infants reared in orphanages, collective settlements, and families, carried through 18 months of age.

KUNST, M. S. A study of thumb and finger sucking in infants. *Psychological Monographs*, 1948, *62(3)*, 1–71. The effect of hunger on thumb sucking.

KUO, Z. *The Dynamics of behavior development: An epigenetic view.* New York: Random House, 1967.

LEVY, D. M. Experiments on the sucking reflex and social behavior of dogs. *American Journal of Orthopsychiatry*, 1934, *4*, 203–224. Levy's experiment with the effects of slow and rapid feeding on non-nutritive sucking.

———. *Maternal overprotection.* New York: Columbia University Press, 1943. Detailed case studies of overprotected children.

———. The infant's memory of inoculation: A contribution to public health procedures. *Journal of Genetic Psychology,* 1960, *96,* 3-46. Crying in reaction to the sight of the needle as a clue to the development of visual memory.

MASON, W. A The effects of environmental relocation on the social development of rhesus monkeys. In C. H. Southwick (Ed.), *Primate social behavior.* Princeton: Van Nostrand, 1963. Pp. 161–173. Effects of social isolation on sexual and other forms of other social behavior.

SCHEIN, M. W. On the irreversibility of imprinting. *Zeitschrift für Tierpsychologie* 1963, *20,* 462-467. Experiments with sexual preferences of turkeys imprinted on human beings and other turkeys.

SCHNEIRLA, T. C., and ROSENBLATT, J. S. Behavioral organization and genesis of the social bond in insects and mammals. *American Journal of Orthopsychiatry* 1961, *31,* 223–253. Contains an account of effects of rearing kittens on a brooder upon later suckling on the mother.

SCOTT, J. P Agonistic behavior of mice and rats: A review. *American Zoologist,* 1966, *6,* 683–701. A review of experimental work on various factors which influence the occurrence of fighting behavior in these animals.

SCOTT, J. P., ROSS, S., FISHER, A. E., and KING, D. J. The effects of early enforced weaning on the sucking behavior of puppies. *Journal of Genetic Psychology,* 1959, *95,* 261–281. Non-nutritive sucking is associated with scheduled feeding, irrespective of whether the puppies are underfed or overfed.

SEARS, R. R., WHITING, J. W. M., NOWLIS, V., and SEARS, P. S. Some child rearing antecedents of aggression and dependency in young children. *Genetic Psychology Monographs,* 1953, *47,* 135–234. Little effect of scheduled feeding, weaning, toilet training, infancy frustration and infant-feeding frustration on aggression as observed in nursery school children.

CHAPTER 6: Stimulation, Practice, and Enrichment

ARSHAVSKY, I. A. Physiological mechanisms of disorders of growth and development due to stress effects in early age periods. In S. Kazda and V. H. Denenberg (Eds.) Postnatal development of phenotype. London Butterworths, 1968, in press.

BENNETT, E. L., DIAMOND, M. C., KRECH, D., and ROSENZWEIG, M. R. Chemical and anatomical plasticity of the brain. *Science,* 1964, *146,* 610–619. Review of experiments on the effects of stimulation on brain size and chemical composition.

CAMPBELL, B. A. Development studies of learning and motivation in infra-primate mammals. In H. W. Stevenson, E. H. Hess, and H. L. Rhein-gold (Eds.), *Early behavior: Comparative and developmental ap-proaches.* New York: Wiley, 1967. Pp. 43–71. Review of work on the general problem of the effect of age on learning ability, especially in rats. Some unexpected results show that fear responses are retained more poorly by young rats than by mature ones.

DENENBERG, V. H. Stimulation in infancy, emotional reactivity, and exploratory behavior. In D. H. Glass (Ed.), *Biology and behavior: Neurophysiology and emotion.* New York: Russel Sage Foundation and Rockefeller University Press, 1967. Review of the effects of infantile stimulation on rats.

GESELL, A., et al. *The first five years of life.* New York: Harper, 1940. Sum-marizes the Gesell studies, emphasizing early motor development.

LEVINE, S. The effects of infantile experience on adult behavior. In A. J. Bachrach (Ed.), *Experimental foundations of clinical psychology.* New York: Basic Books, 1962. Pp. 139–169. Review of work on early stimulation.

LEVINE, S., and MULLINS, R. F. Hormonal influences on brain organization in infant rats. *Science*, 1966, *152*, 1585–1592. Gonadal and adrenal hormones present during critical periods of development may exert a direct action on the central nervous system, affecting later sexual be-havior and other emotional reactions.

NEWTON, G. and LEVINE, S. (Eds.), *Early experience and behavior.* Springfield, Ill.: Thomas, 1967. Review articles by many authors on various aspects of human and animal research.

RIESEN, A. H. Stimulation as a requirement for growth and function in be-havioral development. In D. W. Fiske and S. R. Maddi (Eds.), *Func-tions of varied experience.* Homewood, Ill.: Dorsey, 1961a. Pp. 57–80. General review of effects of visual stimulation.

SWIFT, J. W. Effects of early group experience: The nursery school and day nursery. In M. L. Hoffman and L. W. Hoffman (Eds.), *Review of child development*, Vol. I. New York: Russell Sage Foundation, 1964. Pp. 249–288. Review of the effects of nursery-school experience.

THORPE, W. H. The ontogeny of behavior. In J. A. Moore (Ed.), *Ideas in modern biology.* Garden City, N. Y.: Natural History Press, 1965. Pp. 483–518. Description of critical periods for learning bird songs.

Special Topics

BARON, A., ANTONITIS, J. J., and SCHELL, S. F. Effects of early restriction and facilitation of climbing on later climbing behavior of mice. *Journal of Comparative and Physiological Psychology*, 1962, *55*, 808–812. No critical period in mice for developing this ability.

BAYLEY, N. A study of crying of infants during mental and physical tests. *Journal of Genetic Psychology*, 1932, 40, 306–329. One of the classical studies of crying behavior.

CANDLAND, D. K., and CAMPBELL, B. A. Development of fear in the rat as measured by behavior in the open field. *Journal of Comparative and Physiological Psychology*, 1962, 55, 593–596. Development of fear may limit the beneficial effects of a free environment.

DENNIS, W. Causes of retardation among institutional children: Iran. *Journal of Genetic Psychology*, 1960, 96, 47–59. Case of extreme motor retardation in crib-reared children.

FANTZ, R. L. Ontogeny of perception. In A. M. Schrier, H. F. Harlow, and F. Stollnitz (Eds.), *Behavior of non-human primates*. New York: Academic Press, 1965. Pp. 365–403. Effects of visual deprivation on visual fixation and visual cliff behavior in infant primates.

FORGAYS, D. G., and READ, J. M. Crucial periods for free-environmental experience in the rat. *Journal of Comparative and Physiological Psychology*, 1962, 55, 816–818.

HEBB, D. O. The effects of early experience on problem-solving at maturity. *American Psychologist*, 1947, 2, 306–307. Abstract of Hebb's first work on the effects of enriching the early environment of rats.

LANDAUER, T. K., and WHITING, J. W. Infantile stimulation and adult stature of human males. *American Anthropologist*, 1964, 66, 1007–1028. Results of a survey of practices in different cultures.

MC GRAW, M. B. Later development of children specially trained during infancy. *Child Development*, 1939, 10, 1–19. Best short summary of the author's work on critical periods of motor learning.

PASAMANICK, B. Comparative study of the behavioral development of Negro infants. *Journal of Genetic Psychology*, 1946, 69, 3–44. Motor development is retarded in institutional infants.

RIESEN, A. H. Studying perceptual development using the technique of sensory deprivation. *Journal of Nervous and Mental Disease*, 1961b, 132, 21–25. Effects of rearing kittens in darkness or diffuse light.

SCHAEFER, T. The search for a critical factor in early handling, some methodological implications. In G. Newton and S. Levine (Eds.), *Early experience and behavior*. Springfield, Ill.: Thomas, 1967. Critical appraisal of research on the effects of early stimulation.

SCOTT, J. P., and BRONSON, F. H. Experimental exploration of the et-epimeletic or care-soliciting behavioral system. In P. H. Leiderman and D. Shapiro (Eds.), *Psychobiological approaches to social behavior*. Stanford: Stanford University Press, 1964. Pp. 174–193. Experiments with the effects of isolation and strange situations on the distress vocalization of puppies.

WALK, R. D., and GIBSON, E. J. A comparative analytical study of visual depth perception. *Psychological Monographs*, 1961, 75(15), 1–44. Animal and human experiments with the visual cliff.

WILLIAMS, J. R., and SCOTT, R. B. Growth and development of Negro infants: Motor development and its relationship to child-rearing practices in two groups of Negro infants. *Child Development*, 1953, 24, 103–121. Children develop faster under permissive types of child rearing rather than when subjected to punitive methods.

AUTHOR INDEX

SUBJECT INDEX

A

Activity characteristic of young
    organisms, 139
Adoption
    emotional disturbance of, 43
    emotional damage from, 74–75
    optimum period for, 74
Adrenal gland, effect of hormones
    on fetus, 55
Age
    at onset of walking, 4
    developmental, measurement of, 2–4
    effect on family relationships, 76–77
    of mother, effect on fetal mortality,
        57–58
Aging, disorganizing processes of, 143
Agonistic behavior
    effects of early experience on,
        103–105
    motivational development, 146
Agonistic behavioral system, 9
Albinism, 49
Allelomimetic behavior
    effects of early experience on,
        101–102
    motivational development, 146
Allelomimetic behavioral system, 9
Altitude, effect on pregnancy, 56–57
Animal experiments, limits of human
    implications, 92
Associational learning
    laws of, 137–139
    opposed to variation process, 140
    produces "freezing" of habituation,
        140
Autism, defect in socialization process,
    72

B

Baboon
    dominance order in, 103
    social organization and development,
        29
Behavior patterns, 8
Behavioral development
    evolution of, 24–29
    study techniques, 2–10
Behavioral systems
    in animal kingdom, 8–9
    order of appearance, 10
Bird song, critical period of learning,
    126
Birds, ecology and behavioral
    development, 26
Birth order, see Ordinal position
Brain, growth through function, 125

C

Care-giving behavior, see Epimeletic
    behavior
Care-soliciting behavior, see
    Et-epimeletic behavior
Cat
    periods of development, 17
    reared in darkness, 113
    response to visual cliff, 114
    sucking behavior in, 95
Chicken
    imprinting, 63
    periods of development, 23–24
    see also Indian jungle fowl

R

Rat
  critical period of learning, 125
  early stimulation effects, 116–118
  effect of early experience, 152
  emotionality, 124
  enriched environment, 123–124
  operant conditioning in, 137
  periods of development, 18–19
  sucking aids digestion, 94
  visual cliff response, 114
Reflexes as indices of sensory capacity, 5
Reinforcement, law of, 138
Restriction
  damaging effects of, 151
  effects on motor development, 121–122
Rhesus monkey
  dominance order in, 103
  maternal behavior affected by isolation, 107
  periods of development, 21
  precocity of, 42
  sexual behavior affected by isolation, 106
  social play effects, 152
Rodents, ecology and behavioral development, 26

S

Sensory capacities
  development of, 5–7
  effect of stimulation on, 112–119
  transition in human infants, 39
Sensory development, human, 34–35

Separation
  effects on dependency, 102
  primary effects, 73–74
Sex
  and family relationships, 76–77
  effects on school behavior, 84–85
  hormonal modification of, 54–55
Sex chromosomes, effects of abnormalities, 48
Sexual behavior, effects of early experience on, 105–107
Sexual behavioral system, 9
Sheep
  ecology and behavioral development, 25
  effects of hand rearing on social behavior, 62, 101, 107
  periods of development, 19–20
  primary socialization in, 64
  size of mother and offspring, 54
  social organization and development, 28
  visual cliff response, 5
Shelter-seeking behavior, motivational development, 146
Shelter-seeking behavioral system, 9
Smile
  development of, 94
  social, 36–38
Social environment
  experimental techniques, 62
  stability of, 61–62
Social motivation, 127–128
Social organization, in relation to behavioral development, 27–29
Social relationships
  broken, 72–76
  effect of critical periods on formation, 69
  see also Separation